A Discrete-Time Approach
for System Analysis

ELECTRICAL SCIENCE

A Series of Monographs and Texts

Edited by

Henry G. Booker

UNIVERSITY OF CALIFORNIA AT SAN DIEGO
LA JOLLA, CALIFORNIA

Nicholas DeClaris

UNIVERSITY OF MARYLAND
COLLEGE PARK, MARYLAND

A Discrete-Time Approach for System Analysis

MICHEL CUÉNOD
SOCIÉTÉ GÉNÉRALE POUR L'INDUSTRIE
GENÈVE, SWITZERLAND

ALLEN DURLING
DEPARTMENT OF ELECTRICAL ENGINEERING
UNIVERSITY OF FLORIDA
GAINESVILLE, FLORIDA

 1969

ACADEMIC PRESS   New York and London

ACADEMIC PRESS, INC.
111 Fifth Avenue, New York, New York 10003

United Kingdom Edition published by
ACADEMIC PRESS, INC. (LONDON) LTD.
Berkeley Square House, London W.1

THIS WORK WAS SUPPORTED IN PART BY THE
NATIONAL SCIENCE FOUNDATION UNDER GRANT NO. GK-268.

LIBRARY OF CONGRESS CATALOG CARD NUMBER: 68-23481

PRINTED IN THE UNITED STATES OF AMERICA

To Jacqueline and Patricia

Preface

In recent years the development of complex systems has involved increasingly complicated computation. Extreme growth in sophistication of digital computers has made it possible to apply techniques of numerical analysis to engineering problems that were previously unsolvable, solely because of the tediousness of the solution.

This book is intended to provide the engineer with an introduction to some techniques for finding solutions of certain time-invariant, time-varying, and nonlinear differential equations arising in physical systems. Frequently these equations cannot be solved exactly, and we must settle for an approximate solution. Even when an analytical solution is possible, approximate solutions often provide more insight into the problem than a complex solution in terms of tabulated mathematical functions. We have attempted to present the basic concept of a discrete time approach for system analysis, called "impulse analysis," or "analysis with number series," or "analysis with time series," as applied to the solution of practical engineering problems. With few exceptions we present no new techniques. We have attempted to give a structured presentation of the material with numerous examples and problems.

This book has been written by engineers for engineers. We have based the text more upon empiricism and intuition and less on the mathematical basis that characterizes the classical development. We hope our readers will not condemn the text for this reason, but rather find it to be a stimulating approach. For it is intuition and understanding that become essential as problems become more complex and convergence proofs and error estimates become even more difficult to obtain.

The importance of numerical techniques in engineering cannot be disputed.

To quote Dr. John Truxal [42]:

> The importance of numerical methods of analysis arises because of the rather broad class of practical network synthesis problems in which it is not possible to phrase the specifications in a neat analytical package. The only feasible solution to many design problems involves the numerical calculation of the response of the system to a known input. The tediousness so often involved in the use of the direct methods of Laplace transform theory makes a simplified analysis essential if the designer is not to be handicapped in the study of a variety of possible configurations.
>
> The increased availability of digital computers has permitted the network synthesis to embrace an entirely new approach to design.

For this text we have used a desk calculator for most examples and problems that emphasize the underlying principles; others were worked on a digital computer. All tabular algorithms may be easily extended to machine computation. A few new ideas have emerged for application to digital computers. However, the methods now in use, for the most part, are generalizations and extensions of the methods designed for hand calculation.

Much research effort has been expended in this area in Europe, the Soviet Union, and the United States. We have attempted to present on an introductory level some of the concepts and applications of this research. The book is the outgrowth of lecture notes for courses given to senior and first year graduate students at the University of Florida. Several of these graduate students have since undertaken research in this area.

Chapters 1–3 present the general concepts of impulse analysis and its relation to numerical analysis, Laplace transform and z-transform theory. The remainder of the book is a presentation of several applications of impulse analysis to control problems: basically, system analysis and identification.

A set of problems related to the subject is added at the end of the text.

This book does not pretend to cover the entire rapidly expanding field of system analysis by a discrete approach. It was written as an introduction to the field, and the authors hope the book will be a stimulation to further research.

We would like to thank Dr. Richard Bellman and Dr. Joseph LaSalle for their suggestions and encouragement to write this book; Dr. Wayne Chen, Chairman of the Department of Electrical Engineering at the University of Florida, for his support and encouragement; Mr. Glenn Tober who worked the majority of the examples and problems; the University of Florida Computing Center for the use of its facilities; and finally the National Science

Foundation for its support of the original portion of this work under grant number GK-268. We would like especially to thank Professor Nicholas DeClaris, whose advice and suggestions were most helpful and stimulating for the authors.

August, 1968

M. Cuénod
A. Durling

Contents

A Discrete-Time Approach
for System Analysis

CHAPTER 1 Basic Concepts of Impulse Analysis

INTRODUCTION

When a system is linear or quasilinear, it is possible to analyze its behavior by decomposing the variation of the different variables of the system into a sum of elementary unit functions, applying functional operations to these functions, and superposing the results. The classical solution is based on assumption of a limit as the unit function becomes infinitesimally small.

Another approach is to use sinusoidal functions as unit functions, thus leading to the well-known *spectral analysis.*

A third approach is to use as unit functions a sequence of impulses over a finite interval. The shape of the impulses does not affect the principle of the "*impulse analysis,*" which is the name given to the third approach.

This chapter presents several different unit functions that are used in practice, describes how to obtain a closed form for the sequence of unit functions by using the E- and the z-transforms, and compares some aspects of spectral analysis and impulse analysis. Some aspects of interpolation between sampled data of the functions are also considered by impulse analysis techniques.

1.1 UNIT FUNCTIONS

It is frequently desired to approximate functions of an independent variable by the sum of elementary functions. This usually occurs when the function is known only at a discrete set of values (sample points) of the independent variable or for the application of digital techniques to continuous systems.

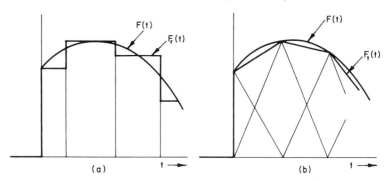

FIG. **1.1**   Functional approximation. (a) Rectangular approximation $F_r(t)$ of the function $F(t)$. (b) Trapezoidal approximation $F_t(t)$ of the function $F(t)$.

This representation is approximate because the values of the function are not known between the sample points.

The most frequently used approximations are the representation of the functions as a series of rectangular or trapezoidal pulses, as shown in Fig. 1.1.

For the rectangular pulse representation the basic building block is the unit rectangular function $I_r(t)$:

$$I_r(t) = \frac{1}{\tau}\left[u\left(t + \frac{\tau}{2}\right) - u\left(t - \frac{\tau}{2}\right)\right]$$

where $u(t)$ is the unit step function and τ is the sampling interval.

The unit triangular function (or merely unit triangle) is defined as

$$I_t(t) = \begin{cases} \dfrac{1}{\tau}\left[1 - \dfrac{|t|}{\tau}\right], & \text{for } |t| < \tau \\ 0, & \text{for } |t| > \tau \end{cases}$$

These unit functions are represented in Fig. 1.2. Some alternative unit

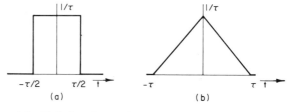

FIG. **1.2**   Unit functions. (a) Unit rectangle. (b) Unit triangle.

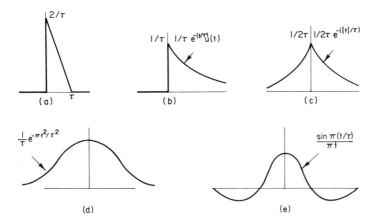

FIG. **1.3**   Unit functions.

functions are presented in Fig. 1.3. Note that the unit functions in Figs. 1.2 and 1.3(a), (b), and (c) satisfy the conditions

$$\int_{-\infty}^{\infty} I(t)\, dt = 1$$

and with the exception of Fig. 1.3(e),

$$\lim_{\tau \to 0} I(t) = 0, \qquad \text{for } t \neq 0$$

Thus for these cases we have

$$\lim_{\tau \to 0} I(t) = \delta(t) \quad \text{[unit impulse or Dirac delta function]}$$

In addition to the above alternatives, it will be useful occasionally to refer to the unit step $u(t)$ and ramp $(t/\tau)u(t)$ functions depicted in Fig. 1.4(a) and (b), respectively.

Hereafter a unit function multiplied by a constant $(AI(t))$ will be referred to as an impulse of magnitude A.

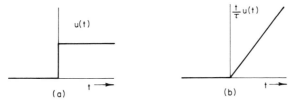

FIG. **1.4**   Unit functions. (a) Unit step. (b) Unit ramp.

1.2   FUNCTIONAL APPROXIMATION AND SEQUENCES

An arbitrary single-valued function $f(t)$ may be approximated by a sequence of impulse functions occurring at increments of the independent variable $[0, \tau, 2\tau, \dots]$ and having magnitudes

$$f_0 = f(0)$$
$$f_1 = f(\tau)$$
$$f_2 = f(2\tau)$$
$$\vdots$$

This approximation is sketched in Fig. 1.5. It is assumed here that the independent variable is time, but any other independent variable may be considered.

The width of the first impulse in Fig. 1.5 is taken to be $\tau/2$. This takes into account the fact that $f(t)$ is zero for $t < 0$. An equivalent representation is to take the first interval equal to τ and $f_0 = f(0)/2$. Hereafter, unless other-wise noted, $f_0 = f(0)$.

Given a real-valued function $f(t)$ defined for $0 \le t \le t_0$, we may extract a sequence of functional values. Thus, for each function $f(t)$ there exists a corresponding sequence of numbers

$$S(F) = [f_0, f_1, f_2, \dots, f_n, \dots] \tag{1.1}$$

and, given an interpolation rule, to each sequence there corresponds a unique function $f(t)$. In particular the sequence of impulse functions (Fig. 1.5) is

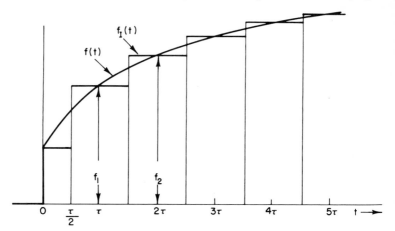

FIG. **1.5**   Functional approximation.

the sequence of functional values for $t = n\tau$ ($n = 0, 1, 2, \ldots$) for some increment size τ. If $t_0 = N\tau$, the sequence will contain $N + 1$ elements and may be regarded as an $N + 1$ dimensional vector. This interpretation will be particularly useful for the matrix representation of convolution and integration.

We shall define several sequences corresponding to a given function $f(t)$.

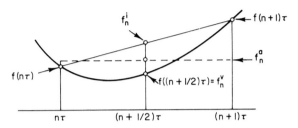

FIG. **1.6**   Definition of the intermediate sequences $S_i(F)$, $S_v(F)$, and $S_a(F)$.

Consider for example the function $f(t)$ in Fig. 1.6. The sequence $S(F)$ has been defined by Eq. (1.1) to be

$$S(F) = [f_0, f_1, f_2, \ldots, f_n, \ldots]$$

where

$$f_0 = f(0), \qquad f_1 = f(\tau), \qquad \text{etc.}$$

The "intermediate value sequence" ($S_v(F)$) is defined as the sequence of the actual values of the function for the intermediate points of the independent variable. That is,

$$S_v(F) = [f_0^v, f_1^v, \ldots, f_n^v, \ldots]$$

where

$$f_n^v = f\left(\frac{2n + 1}{2}\tau\right) = f\left(\left(n + \frac{1}{2}\right)\tau\right)$$

(1.2)

The "intermediate linear interpolating sequence" is defined

$$S_i(F) = [f_0^i, f_1^i, \ldots, f_n^i, \ldots]$$

where

$$f_n^i = \frac{f(n\tau) + f((n + 1)\tau)}{2}.$$

(1.3)

This sequence is given by the mean value of two following terms of $S(F)$. The "intermediate area sequence" ($S_a(F)$) is defined by

$$S_a(F) = [f_0{}^a, f_1{}^a, \ldots, f_n{}^a, \ldots]$$

where

$$f_n{}^a = \frac{1}{\tau} \int_{n\tau}^{(n+1)\tau} f(t)\, dt$$

$$(1.4)$$

If τ is sufficiently small so that $f(t)$ may be considered a quadratic parabola in each increment $k\tau \leq t \leq (k+1)\tau$, by Simpson's 1/3 rule, we have

$$\int_{k\tau}^{(k+1)\tau} f(t)\, dt = \frac{\tau}{2} \left[\frac{1}{3} \left(f(k\tau) + 4f\left(\left(k + \frac{1}{2}\right)\tau\right) + f((k+1)\tau) \right) \right]$$

which is exact for $f(t) = at^2 + bt + c$ in the interval. Thus

$$f_k{}^a = \frac{\tau}{6} \left[f(k\tau) + 4f\left(\left(k + \frac{1}{2}\right)\tau\right) + f((k+1)\tau) \right] \qquad (1.5)$$

Note that

$$f_k{}^a = \frac{1}{6} [f_k + 4f_k{}^v + f_{k+1}]$$

$$= \frac{1}{3} \left[2f_k{}^v + \frac{f_k + f_{k+1}}{2} \right]$$

$$= \frac{1}{3} [2f_k{}^v + f_k{}^i] \qquad (1.6)$$

Thus, for operations where the area under the curve is of importance, it is appropriate to take this weighted average of the intermediate linear interpolating sequence and the intermediate value sequence.

The *step* and *ramp sequences* are defined as the sequences of the magnitudes of steps and ramps required to approximate the function, as shown in Figs. 1.7(a) and (b), respectively. For the step sequence we have

$$f(t) \approx f_0 I(t) + (f_1 - f_0)I(t - \tau) + (f_2 - f_1)I(t - 2\tau) + \cdots$$

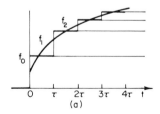 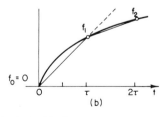

FIG. 1.7 Step and ramp approximations.

where $I(t) = u(t)$ and the f_n may be taken as the terms of any of the intermediate sequences $(f_n{}^i, f_n{}^v, f_n{}^a)$.

where
$$S_e(F) = [f_0{}^e, f_1{}^e, \ldots, f_n{}^e, \ldots]$$

$$f_n{}^e = f_n - \sum_{i=0}^{n-1} f_i{}^e = f_n - f_{n-1}$$

$$\left.\right\} \quad (1.7)$$

Clearly, this yields the approximation shown in Fig. 1.7(a).

For the ramp sequence we have (for $f_0 = 0$)

$$
\begin{aligned}
f(t) &\approx (f_1 - f_0)I(t) + (f_2 - f_1 - (f_1 - f_0))I(t - \tau) \\
&\quad + (f_3 - f_2 - (f_2 - f_1 - (f_1 - f_0)))I(t - 2\tau) + \cdots \\
&= (f_1 - f_0)I(t) + (f_2 - 2f_1 + f_0)I(t - \tau) \\
&\quad + (f_3 - 2f_2 + 2f_1 - f_0)I(t - 2\tau) + \cdots
\end{aligned}
$$

where $I(t) = (t/\tau)u(t)$ or

where
$$S_r(F) = [f_0{}^r, f_1{}^r, \ldots, f_n{}^r, \ldots]$$

$$f_n{}^r = f_n + 2\sum_{k=1}^{n-1} (-1)^k f_k + (-1)^n f_0$$

$$\left.\right\} \quad (1.8)$$

Clearly, the sequence $S_r(F)$ represents the function $f(t)$ by linear segments connecting the data points.

1.3   THE E- AND z-TRANSFORMS

Shifting operators are useful in impulse analysis and will be used extensively.

Multiplication by the E-operator corresponds to a backward shift or delay of one sample increment. The E-operator is defined by the relation

$$Ef(t) = f(t - \tau) \qquad (1.9)$$

The z-operator is defined by the relation

$$zf(t) = f(t + \tau) \qquad (1.10)$$

The E- and z-operators are inverse operators in that

$$Ezf(t) = E(zf(t)) = z(Ef(t)) = f(t)$$

or $E = z^{-1}$. These operators are represented in Fig. 1.8.

Repeated application of a shifting operator yields

$$z^n f(t) = z^{n-1}(zf(t)) = z^{n-1}f(t + \tau) = f(t + n\tau)$$

and

$$E^n f(t) = f(t - n\tau)$$

From the definition of the sequence $S(f)$ we have

$$f(t) \approx \tau\left[f_0 I(t) + Ef_1 I(t) + E^2 f_2 I(t) + \cdots + E^n f_n I(t) + \cdots\right] - \frac{\tau f_0}{2} I(t)$$

$$\approx \tau\left(\sum_{n=0}^{\infty} f_n I(t)E^n\right) - \frac{\tau f_0}{2} I(t)$$

Hereafter the unit impulse will be assumed in expressions of the above form and we shall write

$$f(t) \approx \tau\left(\sum_{n=0}^{\infty} f_n E^n\right) - \frac{\tau f_0}{2}$$

and

$$f(t) \approx \tau\left(\sum_{n=0}^{\infty} f_n z^{-n}\right) - \frac{\tau f_0}{2}$$

Frequently the term $\tau f_0/2$ may be neglected. If this term is neglected, the resultant expressions are known† as the *E-transform* $F(E)$ and the *z-transform* $F(z)$ of $f(t)$‡:

$$F(E) = \tau \sum_{n=0}^{\infty} f_n E^n \qquad (1.11)$$

$$F(z) = \tau \sum_{n=0}^{\infty} f_n z^{-n} \qquad (1.12)$$

---

† Consistent with "common usage" we write $F(E)$ and $F(z)$, realizing that these are not the same functions with different arguments and that $F(z)$ cannot be obtained by substitution of z for E in $F(E)$.

‡ Many authors define the z-transform to be

$$F(z) = \sum_{n=0}^{\infty} f_n z^{-n}$$

The choice of including the factor τ in the definition is motivated by the representation of the function $f(t)$ by a sequence of impulses of strength τf_n. Other advantages of this formulation will become clear in Sec. 2.2.

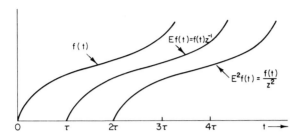

FIG. **1.8**   *E*- and *z*-operators.

Frequently it is possible to express the *E*- and *z*-transforms in closed form as shown in the following examples.

EXAMPLE 1.1

Consider the unit step function

$$u(t) = \begin{cases} 0, & t < 0 \\ 1, & t \geq 0 \end{cases}$$

We have the sequence $S(F)$:

$$S(u) = [1, 1, 1, \ldots] - 0.5$$
$$= [0.5, 1, 1, \ldots]$$

and

$$u(E) = \tau[0.5 + E + E^2 + \cdots]$$
$$u(z) = \tau[0.5 + z^{-1} + z^{-2} + \cdots]$$

It is easy to show by long division† that the series $u(E)$ has the closed form

$$u(E) = \tau[0.5 + E + E^2 + \cdots] = \frac{\tau}{2}\frac{1 + E}{1 - E}$$

---

† Long division:

$$\frac{1 + E}{1 - E}$$
$$\overline{\quad 2E \quad}$$
$$\frac{2E - 2E^2}{2E^2}$$

$$\frac{1 - E}{\begin{array}{l} 1 + 2E + 2E^2 + \cdots \\ = 2(0.5 + E + E^2 + \cdots) \end{array}}$$

If the correction term $\tau f_0/2$ is neglected, we have $u_0 = 1$ and

$$u(E) = \tau[1 + E + E^2 + \cdots] = \frac{\tau}{1 - E}$$

and

$$u(z) = \tau[1 + z^{-1} + z^{-2} + \cdots] = \frac{\tau z}{z - 1}$$

This is, of course, not so accurate an approximation for $u(t)$ as when the $\tau f_0/2$ term is taken into account.

EXAMPLE 1.2

Suppose $f(t) = e^{-at}u(t)$; then

$$F(E) = \tau[1 + Ee^{-a\tau} + E^2 e^{-2a\tau} + \cdots] = \frac{\tau}{1 - Ee^{-a\tau}}$$

and

$$F(z) = \tau\left[1 + \frac{e^{-a\tau}}{z} + \frac{e^{-2a\tau}}{z^2} + \cdots\right] = \frac{z\tau}{z - e^{-a\tau}}$$

EXAMPLE 1.3

Suppose $f(t) = tu(t)$; then

$$S(F) = \tau[0, \tau, 2\tau, 3\tau, \ldots]$$

and

$$F(E) = \tau^2[E + 2E^2 + 3E^3 + \cdots] = \frac{\tau^2 E}{1 - 2E + E^2} = \frac{\tau^2 E}{(1 - E)^2}$$

$$F(z) = \tau^2\left[\frac{1}{z} + \frac{2}{z^2} + \frac{3}{z^3} + \cdots\right] = \frac{\tau^2 z}{(z - 1)^2}$$

Although the sequence representation $S(F)$ and the series representations $F(E)$ and $F(z)$ are equivalent, frequently it is more advantageous to use one than the other. The series representations may in some cases be represented in closed form, and usually the sequence representation is best suited for computation.

In sequence notation the shift or delay operation is defined by the following relations:

$$S(F) = [f_0, f_1, f_2, \ldots]$$
$$S(F)D(-1) = [0, f_0, f_1, f_2, \ldots]$$
$$S(F)D(-n) = [0, 0, \ldots, 0, f_0, f_1, f_2, \ldots] \qquad (n \text{ zeros})$$
$$S(F)D(n) = [f_{n-1}, f_n, f_{n+1}, \ldots]$$

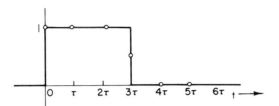

FIG. 1.9 $S(G) = [1, 1, 1, \frac{1}{2}, 0, 0, \cdots]$.

A closed-form approximation may be obtained by the z-transform–Padé approximation. This procedure represents $G(z)$ by a rational function in z, which coincides exactly with $G(z)$ for the first n sample instants. The procedure will be presented by application to an example. Suppose $S(G) = [1, 1, 1, \frac{1}{2}, 0, 0, \ldots]$, which may correspond to the pulse shown in Fig. 1.9. Then

$$G(z) = 1 + z^{-1} + z^{-2} + \tfrac{1}{2}z^{-3} + f_6 z^{-6} + \cdots$$

The approximation equation is

$$G_A(z) = \frac{a_3 z^3 + a_2 z^2 + a_1 z}{z^3 + \alpha_2 z^2 + \alpha_1 z + \alpha_0}$$

Taking $G(z) = G_A(z)$, we have

$$\frac{a_3 z^3 + a_2 z^2 + a_1 z}{z^3 + \alpha_2 z^2 + \alpha_1 z + \alpha_0} = 1 + z^{-1} + z^{-2} + \frac{1}{2} z^{-3} + f_6 z^{-6} + \cdots$$

or

$$a_3 z^3 + a_2 z^2 + a_1 z = z^3 + (1 + \alpha_2)z^2 + (1 + \alpha_2 + \alpha_1)z$$
$$+ \left(\frac{1}{2} + \alpha_2 + \alpha_1 + \alpha_0\right) + \left(\frac{\alpha_2}{2} + \alpha_1 + \alpha_0\right)z^{-1}$$
$$+ \left(\frac{\alpha_1}{2} + \alpha_0\right)z^{-2} + \cdots$$

and we obtain the equations

$$a_3 = 1 \qquad\qquad 0 = \frac{1}{2} + \alpha_2 + \alpha_1 + \alpha_0$$

$$a_2 = 1 + \alpha_2 \qquad\qquad 0 = \frac{\alpha_2}{2} + \alpha_1 + \alpha_0$$

$$a_1 = 1 + \alpha_2 + \alpha_1 \qquad 0 = \frac{\alpha_1}{2} + \alpha_0$$

which yield

$$\alpha_0 = -\tfrac{1}{2}, \quad \alpha_1 = 1, \quad \alpha_2 = -1, \quad a_1 = 1, \quad a_2 = 0, \quad a_3 = 1$$

or

$$G_A(z) = \frac{z^3 + z}{z^3 - z^2 + z - \tfrac{1}{2}} = 1 + z^{-1} + z^{-2} + \frac{1}{2} z^{-3} + \frac{1}{4} z^{-6}$$

which, of course, matches $G(z)$ for the first six terms. In general, if

$$G(z) = C_0 + C_1 z^{-1} + C_2 z^{-2} + \cdots$$

and

$$G_A(z) = \frac{a_n z^n + a_{n-1} z^{n-1} + \cdots + a_1 z}{z^n + \alpha_{n-1} z^{n-1} + \cdots + \alpha_1 z + \alpha_0}$$

then the coefficients $a_n, \ldots, a_1, \alpha_{n-1}, \ldots, \alpha_0$ may be obtained by the $2n$ equations

$$
\begin{aligned}
C_0 &= a_n \\
C_0 \alpha_{n-1} + C_1 &= a_{n-1} \\
&\ \ \vdots \\
C_0 \alpha_1 \quad + C_1 \alpha_2 + \cdots + C_{n-2}\alpha_{n-1} \ + C_{n-1} &= a_1 \\
C_0 \alpha_0 \quad + C_1 \alpha_1 + \cdots + C_{n-1}\alpha_{n-1} \ + C_n &= 0 \\
C_1 \alpha_0 \quad + C_2 \alpha_0 + \cdots + C_n \alpha_{n-1} \quad\ + C_{n-1} &= 0 \\
&\ \ \vdots \\
C_n \alpha_0 \quad + C_n \alpha_1 + \cdots + C_{2n-2}\alpha_{n-1} + C_{2n-1} &= 0
\end{aligned}
$$

A closed-form expression may also be obtained by truncating $G(z)$ to form n terms. Thus,

$$G_A(z) = g_0 + g_1 z^{-1} + g_2 z^{-2} + g_3 z^{-3} + \cdots + g_n z^{-n}$$

Then

$$G_A(z) = \frac{g_0 z^n + g_1 z^{n-1} + \cdots + g_n}{z}$$

This yields an approximation that matches the first $n + 1$ terms and is zero elsewhere.

1.4 IMPULSE ANALYSIS AND FREQUENCY ANALYSIS

It is well known that many periodic functions may be represented by a Fourier series of the form

$$f(t) = \frac{A_0}{z} + \sum_{n=1}^{\infty} \left[A_n \cos\left(\frac{2\pi t}{T}\right) + B_n \sin\left(\frac{2\pi t}{T}\right) \right]$$

or

$$f(t) = \sum_{n=-\infty}^{\infty} C_n e^{j2n\pi t/T}$$

These functions ($f(t)$) may be approximated by the truncation of the series. Thus the periodic function is approximated by the finite sum of fundamental functions.

If $f(t)$ is not periodic, it may still be represented by its frequency components. The representation of $f(t)$ by its Fourier, cosine, sine, and Laplace transforms are, respectively,

$$F(s) = \int_{-\infty}^{\infty} f(t)e^{-j2\pi st}\, dt \qquad f(t) = \int_{-\infty}^{\infty} F(s)e^{j2\pi st}\, ds$$

$$F_c(s) = 2\int_{0}^{\infty} f(t)\cos 2\pi st\, dt \qquad f(t) = 2\int_{0}^{\infty} F_c(s)\cos 2\pi st\, ds$$

$$F_s(s) = 2\int_{0}^{\infty} f(t)\sin 2\pi st\, dt \qquad f(t) = 2\int_{0}^{\infty} F_s(s)\sin 2\pi st\, ds$$

$$L(s) = \int_{0}^{\infty} f(t)e^{-st}\, dt \qquad f(t) = \frac{1}{2\pi j}\int_{c-j\infty}^{c+j\infty} L(s)e^{st}\, ds$$

where c is a constant greater than the abscissa of convergence of the integral $\int_0^\infty f(t)e^{-st}\, ds$.

Although the function may be represented by its frequency components, it is difficult to approximate it by taking only a finite set of elementary functions, since the spectrum of $f(t)$ is continuous if $f(t)$ is not periodic.

The approach of impulse analysis is analogous to the representation of periodic functions by a series of sinusoids. However, $f(t)$ need not be periodic, and we have considerable freedom in the selection of the fundamental functions. In Fig. 1.5, the function $f(t)$ was approximated by a sequence of square pulses; it may also be approximated by any polynomial interpolation. It is particularly convenient to select a unit approximating function (or unit impulse) which represents the function in question most accurately with a few terms. For this, of course, experience and judgment are most helpful.

Some advantages of impulse analysis are the use of approximations in the domain of the independent variable and applicability to computation on a stored program machine for repeated or extensive problems.

1.5   INTERPOLATION

It was pointed out in Sec. 1.1 that, given an interpolation scheme, to each sequence there exists a unique function. Usually the sample increment is sufficiently small so that linear interpolation will yield reasonable accuracy. In practice the data points are frequently "connected" graphically into a "smooth" curve. However, interpolation with a digital computer does not allow this graphical approach, and it is occasionally desirable to go beyond the linear interpolation used in hand computation.

This section is limited to interpolation with polynomials, and examples where intermediate values are desired will be worked by polynomial interpolation. The reader is referred to any standard book on numerical analysis for other interpolation schemes.

An interpolating polynomial is that (nth degree) polynomial $p(t)$ with the property

$$P(t_i) = f(t_i) = f_i \qquad (i = 0, 1, 2, \ldots, n)$$

where the t_i are the sample points.

The Aitken-Neville† scheme is presented because it is particularly well suited for tabulated data and has several convenient tabular algorithms. For these reasons, it is also well suited for evaluation on a digital computer.

Suppose we have a sequence $S(F)$ of equally spaced sample points where

$$S(F) = [f_0, f_1, f_2, \cdots]$$

as defined in Sec. 1.2 ($f_0 = f(0), f_1 = f(\tau)$, and so forth). To determine the values of $f(t)$ by a linear interpolation between $t = 0$ and $t = \tau$, we have

$$P(t) = \frac{1}{\tau} [(f_0)(\tau - t) - (f_1)(0 - t)]$$

Written in determinantal form this is

$$P_{01}(t) = \begin{vmatrix} f_0 & (0 - t) \\ f_1 & (\tau - t) \end{vmatrix}$$

---

† See I. M. Khabaza, "Numerical Analysis." Pergamon Press, Oxford, 1965.

The subscript 01 indicates that $P_{01}(t)$ is the unique (linear) polynomial passing through the points $(0, f_0)$ and (τ, f_1). Likewise, $P_{345}(t)$ is the unique (quadratic) polynomial passing through the points $(3\tau, f_3)$, $(4\tau, f_4)$, and $(5\tau, f_5)$.

It is easy to verify that the polynomial given by the determinant

$$\frac{1}{2\tau} \begin{vmatrix} P_{01}(t) & (0 - t) \\ P_{12}(t) & (2\tau - t) \end{vmatrix}$$

is in fact $P_{012}(t)$. In general,

$$P_{k\cdots n}(t) = \frac{1}{(n - k)\tau} \begin{vmatrix} P_{k\cdots n-1}(t) & (k\tau - t) \\ P_{k+1\cdots n}(t) & (n\tau - t) \end{vmatrix}$$

The sequential computation of the interpolating polynomials may be carried out by the following algorithm.

$$
\begin{array}{cccccc}
0 & f_0 & & & & \\
  &   & P_{01}(t) & & & \\
\tau & f_1 & & P_{012}(t) & & \\
  &   & P_{12}(t) & & P_{0123}(t) & \\
2\tau & f_2 & & P_{123}(t) & & P_{01234}(t) \\
  &   & P_{23}(t) & & P_{1234}(t) & \vdots \\
3\tau & f_3 & & P_{234}(t) & \vdots & \\
  &   & P_{34}(t) & \vdots & & \\
4\tau & f_4 & \vdots & & & \\
  & \vdots & & & &
\end{array}
$$

TABLE 1.1

EXAMPLE OF THE SEQUENTIAL COMPUTATION OF AN INTERPOLATING POLYNOMIAL
BY THE AITKEN-NEVILLE SCHEME

t	e^{-t}	$P_{01}P_{12}P_{23}$	$P_{012}P_{123}$	P_{0123}
0	1.0			
		$P_{01}(t) = 1 - 0.63212t$		
1	0.36788		$P_{012}(t) = 1 - 0.83191t + 0.19979t^2$	
		$P_{12}(t) = 0.60042 - 0.23254t$		$P_{0123}(t) = \begin{cases} 1 - 0.91611t \\ +0.32609t^2 - 0.04210t^3 \end{cases}$
2	0.13534		$P_{123}(t) = 0.74741 - 0.45302t + 0.07350t^2$	
		$P_{23}(t) = 0.30644 - 0.08555t$		
3	0.04979			

For example, $P_{01}(t)$, $P_{012}(t)$, and $P_{0123}(t)$ for $f(t) = e^{-t}$ with $t = 1$ are presented in Table 1.1. For the point $t = 0.5$ we have

$$P_{01}(0.5) = 0.68394$$
$$P_{012}(0.5) = 0.63399$$
$$P_{0123}(0.5) = 0.61820$$
$$f(0.5) = 0.60653$$

CHAPTER 2 Operations with Impulse Analysis

INTRODUCTION

This chapter presents functional operations with the use of sequences of unit functions as defined in Chapter 1, namely: addition, subtraction, multiplication, convolution, deconvolution, integration, and differentiation.

2.1 ADDITION, SUBTRACTION, MULTIPLICATION

The operations of addition, subtraction, and multiplication of two sequences are analogous to the addition, subtraction, and inner product of two vectors. Given the functions $f(t)$ and $g(t)$, we have

$$S(F \pm G) = S(F) \pm S(G)$$
$$= [f_0 \pm g_0, f_1 \pm g_1, \ldots, f_n \pm g_n, \ldots]$$

$$F(E) \pm G(E) = \tau \sum_{n=0}^{\infty} (f_n \pm g_n)E^n$$

$$F(z) \pm G(z) = \tau \sum_{n=0}^{\infty} (f_n \pm g_n)z^{-n}$$

EXAMPLE 2.1

$$S(F) = [1, 3, 2]$$
$$S(G) = [1, 5, 7, 3, 2, 1]$$
$$S(F) + S(G) = [2, 8, 9, 3, 2, 1]$$

The product of two sequences is given by

$$S(F)S(G) = [f_0 g_0, f_1 g_1, \ldots, f_n g_n, \ldots]$$

$$FG(E) = \tau \sum_{n=0}^{\infty} f_n g_n E^n$$

$$FG(z) = \tau \sum_{n=0}^{\infty} f_n g_n z^{-n}$$

The E- and z-transform representation of the product $f(t)g(t)$ is written $FG(E)$ and $FG(z)$ to distinguish it from the product $F(E)G(E)$.

In matrix notation the multiplication operation is written

$$[f] \times [\backslash^g] = [f_0 g_0, f_1 g_1, \ldots]$$

where

$$[f] = [f_0, f_1, f_2, \ldots] \quad \text{and} \quad [\backslash^g] = \begin{bmatrix} g_0 & 0 & \cdots \\ 0 & g_1 & \\ \vdots & & \ddots \end{bmatrix}$$

2.2   CONVOLUTION

2.2.1   The Convolution Operation

Consider a linear system with input $a(t)$, output $b(t)$, and impulse response $g(t)$. (See Fig. 2.1.)

Suppose the input is the unit rectangular impulse

$$a(t) = I_r(t) = \frac{1}{\tau}\left[u\left(t + \frac{\tau}{2}\right) - u\left(t - \frac{\tau}{2}\right)\right]$$

Then for τ sufficiently small, the output is the impulse response

$$b(t) \approx g(t)$$

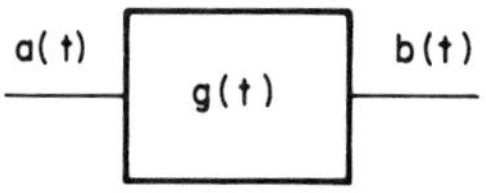

FIG. **2.1**   Linear system representation.

For arbitrary $a(t)$ we may again write

$$a(t) \approx \tau \sum_{n=0}^{\infty} a_n I_r(t) E^n - \frac{\tau a_0}{2} I_r(t)$$

Neglecting the term $(\tau a_0/2)I_r(t)$, we have

$$a(t) \approx \tau \sum_{n=0}^{\infty} a_n E^n I_r(t)$$

The system response to $\tau a_n E^n I_r(t) = \tau a_n I_r(t - n\tau)$ is (for small τ) equal to $\tau a_n g(t - n\tau)$, and $b(t)$ at $t = k\tau$ is the superposition of these impulse responses up to and including $k\tau$. Thus

$$b(k\tau) = \tau \sum_{n=0}^{k} a_n g(k\tau - n\tau) = \tau \sum_{n=0}^{k} a_n g_{k-n} \qquad (2.1)$$

In sequence notation we write

$$S(B) = \tau S(A) * S(G)$$

This expression for $b(k\tau)$ indicates that the response is the summation of past and present inputs, each weighted by the response to an impulse applied at that time. For this reason the impulse response is frequently referred to as the "weighting function."

Letting $n\tau = x$ and $k\tau = t_0$, from Eq. (2.1) we have

$$b(t_0) = \sum_{n=0}^{k} a(x) g(t_0 - x) \, \Delta x$$

where

$$\Delta x = x_n - x_{n-1} = n\tau - (n-1)\tau = \tau$$

Taking the limit as $\tau \to 0$, we have

$$b(t_0) = \lim_{\substack{\tau \to 0 \\ (k=t_0/\tau)}} \sum_{n=0}^{k} a(x) g(t_0 - x) \, \Delta x$$

$$= \int_0^{t_0} a(x) g(t_0 - x) \, dx$$

or

$$b(t) = a(t) * g(t)$$

If $g(t) = 0$ for $t < 0$, we have

$$b(t) = \int_0^t a(x)g(t - x)\,dx \tag{2.2}$$

which is the well-known "*convolution*," or "*Duhamel integral*."

In sequence notation we have

$$S(A) = [a_0, a_1, a_2, \ldots]$$
$$S(G) = [g_0, g_1, g_2, \ldots]$$

and, from Eq. (2.1),

$$S(B) = \tau S(A) * S(G)$$

$$= \tau\left[a_0 g_0,\ a_1 g_0 + a_0 g_1,\ \ldots,\ \left(\sum_{k=0}^{n} a_k g_{n-k}\right)\cdots\right]$$

The sequence convolution may be tabulated by the following algorithm

$S(A) =$	a_0	a_1	a_2	a_3	$\cdots$
$S(G)$					
$\quad = g_0$	$a_0 g_0$	$a_1 g_0$	$a_2 g_0$	$a_3 g_0$	$\cdots$
$\quad = g_1$		$a_0 g_1$	$a_1 g_1$	$a_2 g_1$	$\cdots$
$\quad = g_2$			$a_0 g_2$	$a_1 g_2$	$\cdots$
$\quad \vdots$				$\vdots$	

$$\tau S(A) * S(G) = S(B) = \tau[a_0 g_0,\ (a_0 g_1 + a_1 g_0),\ (a_0 g_2 + a_1 g_1 + a_2 g_0)\cdots]$$

For example, take

$$S(A) = [1, 2, 3, 1]$$
$$S(G) = [1, 2, 1]$$
$$\tau = 1$$

$S(A) =$	1	2	3	1		
$S(G)$						
$\quad = 1$	1	2	3	1		
$\quad = 2$		2	4	6	2	
$\quad = 1$			1	2	3	1

$$S(B) = \qquad [1, 4, 8, 9, 5, 1]$$

Note that the result of the convolution is a sequence longer than either of its component sequences, the number of terms in $S(B)$ being equal to one

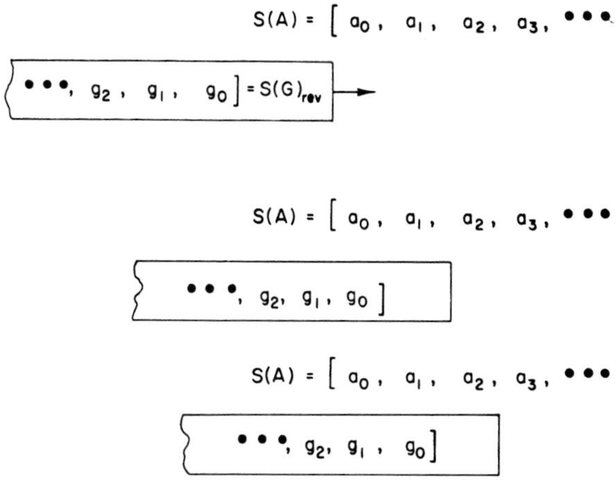

$$S(A) = \begin{bmatrix} a_0, & a_1, & a_2, & a_3, & \bullet\bullet\bullet \end{bmatrix}$$

$$\langle \bullet\bullet\bullet, g_2, \ g_1, \ g_0 \end{bmatrix} = S(G)_{\text{rev}} \rightarrow$$

$$S(A) = \begin{bmatrix} a_0, & a_1, & a_2, & a_3, & \bullet\bullet\bullet \end{bmatrix}$$

$$\langle \bullet\bullet\bullet, g_2, \ g_1, \ g_0 \end{bmatrix}$$

$$S(A) = \begin{bmatrix} a_0, & a_1, & a_2, & a_3, & \bullet\bullet\bullet \end{bmatrix}$$

$$\langle \bullet\bullet\bullet, g_2, \ g_1, \ g_0 \end{bmatrix}$$

FIG. **2.2**   Convolution of sequences.

less than the sum of the number of terms in $S(A)$ and $S(G)$. Also, the sum of the terms in $S(B)$ is equal to the product of the sum of the terms in $S(A)$ with the sum of the terms in $S(G)$.

For the preceding example we have for the number of terms in

$$S(A) = 4$$
$$S(G) = 3$$
$$S(B) = 4 + 3 - 1 = 6$$

and for the sum of terms in

$$S(A) = 7$$
$$S(G) = 4$$
$$S(B) = 4 \times 7 = 28$$

These checks are particularly valuable when the convolution is done by hand on a desk calculator.

The tabulation may be simplified by writing one of the sequences on a strip of paper in reverse order and placing it below the other, as in Fig. 2.2.

To determine $(1/\tau)b_n$, we need only place g_0 below a_n and add the vertical products, since

$$b_n = \tau \sum_{n=0}^{n} a_k g_{n-k}$$

The E-transform corresponding to the above convolution is clearly given by

$$B(E) = \tau^2\left[a_0 \sum_{n=0}^{\infty} g_n E^n + a_1 \sum_{n=0}^{\infty} g_n E^{n+1} + \cdots\right]$$

$$= \tau^2 \sum_{n=0}^{\infty} \sum_{m=0}^{\infty} a_m g_n E^{n+m} \tag{2.3}$$

which is the product of the two polynomials $A(E)$ and $G(E)$. Thus $B(E) = A(E)G(E)$.

The sequence convolution may be represented in matrix notation as the product of the row vector $\tau[a_0 \ a_1 \ a_2 \ \cdots]$, with the matrix

$$\begin{bmatrix} g_0 & g_1 & g_2 & \cdots \\ 0 & g_0 & g_1 & \cdots \\ 0 & 0 & g_0 & \cdots \\ \vdots & \vdots & & \end{bmatrix}$$

This multiplication yields

$$[b_0, b_1, b_2, \ldots] = \tau[a_0 g_0, (a_0 g_1 + a_1 g_0), \ldots]$$

If the convolution integration, is carried out by the trapezoidal rule, we have (assuming $a(x) = g(x) = 0$ for $x < 0$ and data points at $t = 0, \tau, 2\tau, \ldots$) that for $t \times 0$,

$$b(0) = \int_0^{\infty} a(x)g(-x)\, dx \approx \frac{\tau a_0 g_0}{2}$$

and for $t = \tau$,

$$b(\tau) = \int_0^{\infty} a(x)g(\tau - x)\, dx \approx \tau\left(\frac{a_0 g_1}{2} + \frac{a_1 g_0}{2}\right)$$

and in general, for $t = n\tau$,

$$b(n\tau) = \int_0^{\infty} a(x)g(n\tau - x)\, dx \approx \tau\left(\frac{a_0 g_n}{2} + a_1 g_{n-1} + \cdots + a_{n-1} g_1 + \frac{a_n g_0}{2}\right)$$

Thus this trapezoidal integration corresponds to the convolution

$$S(B) = S(A) * S(G) + \frac{a_0 g_0}{4} \tag{2.4}$$

where

$$S(A) = \left[\frac{a_0}{2}, a_1, a_2, \ldots\right] \quad \text{and} \quad S(G) = \left[\frac{g_0}{2}, g_1, g_2, \ldots\right]$$

Below is the tabular algorithm associated with the trapezoidal convolution:

	$\frac{a_0}{2}$	a_1	a_2	a_3	$\cdots$
$\frac{g_0}{2}$	$(2)\frac{a_0 g_0}{4}$	$\frac{a_1 g_0}{2}$	$\frac{a_2 g_0}{2}$	$\frac{a_3 g_0}{2}$	$\cdots$
g_1		$\frac{a_0 g_1}{2}$	$a_1 g_1$	$a_2 g_1$	$\cdots$
g_2			$\frac{a_0 g_2}{2}$	$a_1 g_2$	$\cdots$
$\vdots$			$\vdots$		

$$S(B) \times \tau\left[\frac{a_0 g_0}{2}, \frac{a_0 g_1}{2} + \frac{a_1 g_0}{2}, \frac{a_0 g_2}{2} + a_1 g_1 + \frac{a_2 g_0}{2}, \ldots\right]$$

The factor (2) in the first entry of the table takes into account the term $a_0 g_0/4$ to be added to $S(A) * S(G)$.

The trapezoidal integration of the convolution integral

$$b(t) = \int_0^\infty a(x)g(t - x) \, dx$$

may be written in matrix notation as

$$\tau S(A)\mathbf{G} = S(B)$$

where $S(A)$ and $S(B)$ are considered as row vectors and

$$\mathbf{G} = \begin{bmatrix} \frac{g_0}{2} & \frac{g_1}{2} & \frac{g_2}{2} & \frac{g_3}{2} & \frac{g_4}{2} & \cdots \\ 0 & \frac{g_0}{2} & g_1 & g_2 & g_3 & \cdots \\ 0 & 0 & \frac{g_0}{2} & g_1 & g_2 & \cdots \\ 0 & 0 & 0 & \frac{g_0}{2} & g_1 & \cdots \\ \vdots & \vdots & \vdots & \vdots & \vdots & \end{bmatrix}$$

or

$$\tau S(G)\mathbf{A} = S(B)$$

where $S(G)$ and $S(B)$ are row vectors and

$$\mathbf{A} = \begin{bmatrix} \dfrac{a_0}{2} & \dfrac{a_1}{2} & \dfrac{a_2}{2} & \dfrac{a_3}{2} & \dfrac{a_4}{2} & \cdots \\[2ex] 0 & \dfrac{a_0}{2} & a_1 & a_2 & a_3 & \cdots \\[2ex] 0 & 0 & \dfrac{a_0}{2} & a_1 & a_2 & \cdots \\[2ex] 0 & 0 & 0 & \dfrac{a_0}{2} & a_1 & \cdots \\[2ex] \vdots & \vdots & \vdots & \vdots & \vdots \end{bmatrix}$$

This notation is particularly convenient for the evaluation of the convolution integral relating the input and output statistics of linear systems with stationary random inputs. Consider the linear system shown in Fig. 2.1 with input $a(t)$, output $b(t)$, and impulse response $g(t)$. If $a(t)$ is a stationary random process, its autocorrelation function is

$$R_{aa}(\theta) = \lim_{T \to \infty} \frac{1}{2T} \int_{-T}^{T} a(t)a(t + \theta)\, dt$$

The cross-correlation function between input and output is

$$R_{ab}(\theta) = \lim_{T \to \infty} \frac{1}{2T} \int_{-T}^{T} a(t)b(t + \theta)\, dt$$

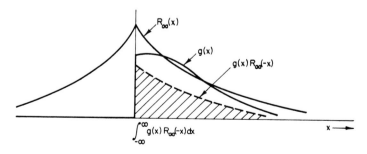

FIG. 2.3 $\int_{-\infty}^{\infty} g(x)R_{aa}(-x)\, dx$.

If the system is a stable, fixed parameter, linear system, we have the relation

$$R_{ab}(\theta) = \int_{-\infty}^{\infty} R_{aa}(\theta - x)g(x)\, dx$$

$$= R_{xx}(\theta) * g(\theta)$$

Since $R_{aa}(\theta)$ is usually nonzero for $\theta < 0$, this convolution may not be performed by the techniques presented above.

It is easy to show that $R_{aa}(\theta)$ is an even function of θ. For $\theta = 0$, it is required to determine the integral depicted in Fig. 2.3.

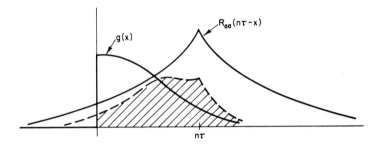

$g(x)$

$R_{aa}(n\tau - x)$

$n\tau$

FIG. 2.4 $\int_{-\infty}^{\infty} g(x)R_{aa}(n\tau - x)\, dx.$

This integration may be performed by trapezoidal integration to obtain

$$R_{ab}(0) \doteq \tau\left[\frac{x_0 g_0}{2} + x_1 g_1 + x_2 g_2 + \cdots\right]$$

where

$$x_k = R_{aa}(k\tau)$$

Figure 2.4 shows the situation for $\theta = n\tau$.
By trapezoidal integration we have

$$R_{ab}(n\tau) \doteq \left[\frac{x_n g_0}{2} + x_{n-1} g_1 + \cdots + x_0 g_n + x_1 g_{n+1} + x_2 g_{n+2} + \cdots\right]$$

Defining the sequence

$$S(Z) = [z_0, z_1, z_2, \ldots]$$

where

$$z_n = R_{ab}(n\tau)$$

we have in matrix notation

$$S(Z) = \tau S(G)\mathbf{A}_x$$

where

$$\mathbf{A}_x = \begin{bmatrix} \dfrac{x_0}{2} & \dfrac{x_1}{2} & \dfrac{x_2}{2} & \dfrac{x_3}{2} & \dfrac{x_4}{2} & \cdots \\[2mm] x_1 & x_0 & x_1 & x_2 & x_3 & \cdots \\[1mm] x_2 & x_1 & x_0 & x_1 & x_2 & \cdots \\[1mm] x_3 & x_2 & x_1 & x_0 & x_1 & \cdots \\[1mm] \vdots & \vdots & \vdots & \vdots & \vdots & \end{bmatrix}$$

If $g_n \doteq x_n \doteq 0$ for $n > k$, we have

$$\mathbf{A}_x = \begin{bmatrix} \dfrac{x_0}{2} & \dfrac{x_1}{2} & \dfrac{x_2}{2} & \dfrac{x_3}{2} & \cdots & \dfrac{x_k}{2} \\[2mm] x_1 & x_0 & x_1 & x_2 & \cdots & x_{k-1} \\[1mm] x_2 & x_1 & x_0 & x_1 & \cdots & x_{k-2} \\[1mm] x_3 & x_2 & x_1 & x_0 & \cdots & x_{k-3} \\[1mm] \vdots & \vdots & \vdots & \vdots & & \vdots \\[1mm] x_k & x_{k-1} & x_{k-2} & x_{k-3} & \cdots & x_0 \end{bmatrix}$$

EXAMPLE 2.2

Suppose

$$g(t) = \tfrac{1}{2}e^{-(t/2)}u(t) \qquad R_{xx}(\theta) = e^{-|\theta|}$$

For $\tau = 1/2$, we have

$S(R_{xx}(\theta)) = [1.0, 0.6065, 0.3679, 0.2231, 0.1353, 0.0821, 0.0498,$
$\qquad\qquad\qquad 0.0302, 0.0183, 0.0111, 0.0067, 0.0041, 0.0025, 0.0015, \ldots]$

$S(G) = [0.5, 0.3894, 0.3033, 0.2362, 0.1837, 0.1433, 0.1116, 0.0869,$
$\qquad\qquad\qquad 0.0677, 0.0527, 0.0410, 0.0320, 0.0249, 0.0194, \ldots]$

Taking

$$\mathbf{A}_x = \begin{bmatrix} \dfrac{x_0}{2} & \dfrac{x_1}{2} & \dfrac{x_2}{2} & \cdots & \dfrac{x_{13}}{2} \\[2mm] x_1 & x_0 & x_1 & \cdots & x_{12} \\[1mm] x_2 & x_1 & x_0 & \cdots & x_{11} \\[1mm] \vdots & \vdots & \vdots & & \vdots \\[1mm] x_{13} & x_{12} & x_{11} & \cdots & x_0 \end{bmatrix}$$

we have

$$S(R_{xy}(\theta)) = S(Z) = \tau S(G)A_x$$
$$= [0.333, 0.432, 0.441, 0.407, 0.355, 0.300, 0.247,$$
$$0.201, 0.162, 0.129, 0.103, 0.081, 0.064, 0.050, \ldots]$$

which compares with the exact sequences of

$$R_{xy}(\theta) = \tfrac{4}{3}e^{-\theta/2} - e^{-\theta}$$

which is quite favorable for this large increment size. Thus

$$S(Z)_{\text{exact}} = [0.349, 0.445, 0.451, 0.415, 0.362, 0.305, 0.252,$$
$$0.205, 0.164, 0.130, 0.102, 0.079, 0.060, 0.042, \ldots]$$

2.2.2 Convolution with Intermediate Sequences

It is well known that the value of a convolution integral depends primarily upon the area (strength or weight) of the functions being integrated. For this reason we might expect the results of the convolution operation to be most accurate if the approximating functions have the same area as the approximated function. Thus it seems reasonable to expect that the use of the intermediate area sequence $S_a(F)$ will be most accurate. It turns out, of course, that this is true

$$S(B) = S_a(A) * S_a(G) \tag{2.5}$$

For the intermediate sequences $(S_v(F), S_i(F), S_a(F))$, the value assigned to the first term approximates the function at $t = \tau/2$ and not $t = 0$, and the nth term most nearly approximates $f((n + \tfrac{1}{2})\tau)$. In terms of the E- and z-transform we have

$$F_v(E) = E^{-\frac{1}{2}}F(E) \qquad \text{and} \qquad F_v(z) = z^{\frac{1}{2}}F(z)$$

When $F(E)$ and $F(z)$ are the E- and z-transforms corresponding to the sequence $S(F)$, $E^{-\frac{1}{2}}$ and $z^{\frac{1}{2}}$ represent a shift of $\tau/2$.

In this notation we have

$$F_v(E)G_v(E) = E^{-1}F(E)G(E)$$

which is the convolution shifted by one period.

Thus, for the convolution using the intermediate sequences for both functions, we obtain a shift of one period. This may be corrected by inserting a zero for the first value in the resultant sequence and shifting each term one position to the right to yield

$$[\alpha_0, \alpha_1, \alpha_2, \ldots] \rightarrow [0, \alpha_0, \alpha_1, \alpha_2, \ldots]$$

denoted $S(\alpha) \rightarrow S(\alpha)D(-1)$ for a delay (shift) of one sample, giving the resultant convolution

$$S(B) = S_v(A) * S_v(G)D(-1) \tag{2.6}$$

An equivalent correction is obtained by taking one of the intermediate sequences with a positive shift of $\tau/2$ and the other with a negative shift of $\tau/2$. This shift is important, but it does not alter the results of the convolution if the final sequence is shifted to its proper position.†

EXAMPLE 2.3

Consider the system in Fig. 2.5 with transfer function $G(s) = 1/(5s + 1)$.

It is desired to determine the step response by numerical convolution. The step response, $b(t) = (1 - e^{-(t/5)})u(t)$, will be used to compare the accuracy of the different methods.

Taking $\tau = 1$, we have $a(t) = u(t)$ and $g(t) = \frac{1}{5}e^{-(t/5)}u(t)$.

$$S(A) = [1, 1, 1, \ldots]$$
$$S_v(A) = S_i(A) = S_a(A) = [0.5, 1, 1, \ldots]$$
$$S(G) = [0.2, 0.163746, 0.134064, \ldots]$$
$$S_v(G) = [0.180967, 0.148164, \ldots]$$
$$S_i(G) = [0.181873, 0.148905, \ldots]$$
$$S_a(G) = [0.181269, 0.148411, \ldots]$$

We obtain for the convolution $S(A) * S(G)$—(only the first few calculations are included)

$S(G) =$	0.2	0.163746	0.134064	0.109762	$\cdots$
$S(A)$					
$= 1$	0.2	0.163746	0.134064	0.109762	
$= 1$		0.2	0.163746	0.134064	
$= 1$			0.2	0.163746	
$\vdots$				0.2	
$S(B) =$	0.2	0.363746	0.497810	0.607572	

---

† This shift of τ is equivalent to interpreting the result as an intermediate sequence shifted by $\tau/2$.

We have

$$S(A) * S(G) = S(B) = [0.2, 0.363746, 0.497810, 0.607572, \ldots]$$

This procedure is carried out for all terms of interest.†

Table 2.1 presents the results of this calculation in using several sequence definitions and the trapezoidal rule.

The error obtained in using the "intermediate value" sequences ($S_v(G)$ and $S_v(A)$) is approximately half the error resulting from the use of the linear interpolating sequences ($S_i(G)$ and $S_i(A)$).

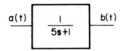

$$a(t) \quad \boxed{\dfrac{1}{5s+1}} \quad b(t)$$

FIG. **2.5** Example system.

The use of the "intermediate area sequence" yields results that differ from the exact values only in the sixth decimal place. For reasonably well-behaved functions, this sequence allows a large increment size for good accuracy. This is demonstrated by the above example with $\tau = 4$. The results of this calculation appear in Table 2.2 and Fig. 2.6(a). Table 2.3 and Fig. 2.6(b) represent the step response for the increment $\tau = 10$. Note that with the increment size (τ) equal to twice the time constant of the system, the use of intermediate area sequences yields a maximum error of only 5 percent. As a rule, the increment size is taken to be about 20 percent of the smallest time constant of the system.

EXAMPLE 2.4

Consider the system in Fig. 2.7(b) with transfer function

$$G(s) = \frac{1}{T_1 s + 1}$$

It is desired to determine the response of this system by numerical convolution to the input $x(t)$ shown in Fig. 2.7(a), with $T_1 = 5$.

Using the same procedure as for Example 2.3, we have the results for $\tau = 1$ tabulated in Table 2.4. The results for $\tau = 2$ are presented in Table

---

† In practice, the first term is usually reduced by the correction term $\tau f_0/2$. This would yield

$$S(A) * S(G) = S(B) = [0.1, 0.363746, 0.497810, 0.607572, \ldots]$$

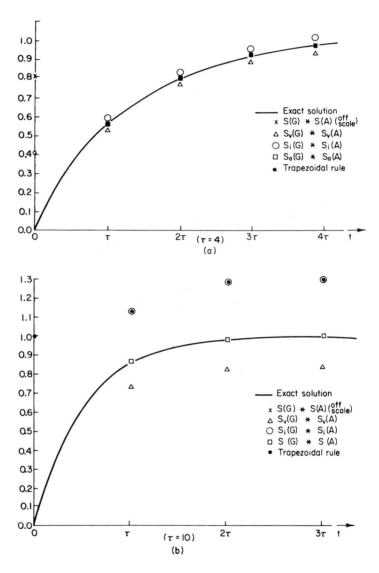

FIG. **2.6** Step response. (a) $\tau = 4$. (b) $\tau = 10$.

TABLE 2.1

Step Response of System Shown in Fig. 2.5 for $(\tau = 1)$

t	$S(B)$ exact solution	$S(G) * S(A)$	$S_v(G) * S_v(A)$	$S_i(G) * S_i(A)$	$S_a(G) * S_a(A)$	Trapezoidal rule
0	0.0	0.200000	0.0	0.0	0.0	0.10000
τ	0.181269	0.363746	0.180967	0.181873	0.181269	0.181873
2τ	0.329680	0.497810	0.329131	0.330778	0.329680	0.330778
3τ	0.451188	0.607572	0.450437	0.452691	0.451188	0.452691
4τ	0.550671	0.697438	0.549754	0.552505	0.550671	0.552505
5τ	0.632121	0.771014	0.631068	0.634226	0.632121	0.634226
6τ	0.698060	0.831253	0.697642	0.701133	0.698806	0.701134
7τ	0.753403	0.880572	0.752148	0.755912	0.753403	0.755913
8τ	0.798103	0.920251	0.796774	0.800761	0.798103	0.800762
9τ	0.834701	0.954011	0.833311	0.837481	0.834701	0.837481
10τ	0.864665	0.981078	0.863225	0.867544	0.864665	0.867545
11τ	0.889197	1.003239	0.887716	0.892158	0.889197	0.892159
12τ	0.909282	1.021383	0.907768	0.012310	0.909282	0.912311
13τ	0.925726	1.036238	0.924185	0.928809	0.925722	0.928811
14τ	0.939190	1.048400	0.937626	0.942317	0.939185	0.942319
15τ	0.950213	1.058357	0.948631	0.953377	0.950205	0.953377

TABLE 2.2

Step Response of System Shown in Fig. 2.5 for ($\tau = 4$)

t	$S(B)$ exact solution	$S(G) * S(A)$	$S_v(G) * S_v(A)$	$S_i(G) * S_i(A)$	$S_a(G) * S_a(A)$	Trapezoidal rule
0	0.0	0.8	0.0	0.0	0.0	0.4
τ	0.550671	1.159464	0.536256	0.579732	0.550748	0.579732
2τ	0.798103	1.32098	0.777212	0.840224	0.798216	0.840224
3τ	0.909282	1.39356	0.885480	0.957272	0.909336	0.957268
4τ	0.959238	1.426164	0.934128	1.009864	0.959300	1.009860

TABLE 2.3

Step Response ($\tau = 10$)

t	$S(B)$ exact solution	$S(G) * S(A)$	$S_v(G) * S_v(A)$	$S_i(G) * S_i(A)$	$S_a(G) * S_a(A)$	Trapezoidal rule
0	0.0	2.0	0.0	0.0	0.0	1.0
τ	0.864665	2.27067	0.73576	1.13534	0.86895	1.135534
2τ	0.981684	2.30730	0.83533	1.28899	0.98655	1.28899
3τ	0.997521	2.31226	0.84881	1.30979	1.00247	1.30978

FIG. **2.7** System for Example 2.5.

2.5 and Fig. 2.8(a). The results for $\tau = 5$ are presented in Table 2.6 and Fig. 2.8(b).

For this example the error is similar to that obtained for Example 2.3. Even with $\tau = 5$ (two time constants) the maximum error, using the intermediate area sequence, is approximately 13 percent. For $\tau = 2$ (approximately one time constant) the maximum error is less than 2.5 percent.

Table 2.7 presents the maximum error obtained for each method applied to Examples 2.3 and 2.4. For those techniques ($S(G) * S(A)$ and trapezoidal rule) where there is a large error in initial values, the maximum error after the first few terms is given.

TABLE 2.7

MAXIMUM PERCENT ERROR FOR EXAMPLES 2.3 AND 2.4

	Percent error					
	Example 1			Example 2		
Convolution technique	$\tau = 1$	$\tau = 4$	$\tau = 10$	$\tau = 1$	$\tau = 2$	$\tau = 5$
$S(G) * S(A)$	13.0 [a]	62.0 [a]	130.0 [a]	31.0 [a]	72.0 [a]	39.0
$S_v(G) * S_v(A)$	0.16	2.6	15.0	1.0	5.0	33.0
$S_i(G) * S_i(A)$	0.32	5.2	32.0	2.0	7.0	64.0
$S_a(G) * S_a(A)$	0.008	0.006	5.0	0.8	2.9	14.0
Trapezoidal rule	0.32 [a]	5.2 [a]	32.0 [a]	1.5 [a]	14.0	39.0

[a] Neglecting large error in first term (or first few terms).

For the examples given above an increment size $\tau = 1$ yields maximum errors of about 1 percent or less. For this reason the results are not plotted. Examination of Tables 2.1 and 2.4 demonstrate the results. For each case this is sufficient engineering accuracy. The examples were tabulated with larger increments only to compare the accuracy of the different methods.

TABLE 2.4

EXAMPLE 2.4   SYSTEM RESPONSE FOR ($\tau = 1$)

t	$S(B)$ exact solution	$S(G) * S(A)$	$S_v(G) * S_v(A)$	$S_i(G) * S(A)$	$S_a(G) * S_a(A)$	Trapezoidal rule
0	0.00000	0.0000	0.0000	0.0000	0.0000	0.0000
τ	0.018731	0.04000	0.018097	0.018187	0.018127	0.02000
2τ	0.070320	0.112749	0.069106	0.069453	0.069222	0.072749
3τ	0.148812	0.212311	0.147064	0.147800	0.147309	0.152311
4τ	0.249329	0.333826	0.247083	0.248319	0.247494	0.253826
5τ	0.367879	0.473313	0.365164	0.366993	0.365774	0.373313
6τ	0.463732	0.547515	0.461842	0.464154	0.462614	0.467515
7τ	0.505957	0.568269	0.504802	0.507329	0.505644	0.508269
8τ	0.504273	0.545170	0.503781	0.506304	0.504622	0.505170
9τ	0.466641	0.486420	0.466751	0.469088	0.467532	0.466420
10τ	0.399577	0.398247	0.400240	0.402243	0.400907	0.398247
11τ	0.327146	0.326057	0.327689	0.329328	0.328235	0.326057
12τ	0.267844	0.266952	0.268288	0.269631	0.268738	0.266952
13τ	0.219293	0.218561	0.219657	0.220759	0.220023	0.218561
14τ	0.179542	0.178945	0.179839	0.180740	0.180139	0.178945
15τ	0.146996	0.146349	0.147243	0.147978	0.147485	0.146349

TABLE 2.5

EXAMPLE 2.4 RESPONSE FOR ($\tau = 2$)

t	$S(B)$ exact solution	$S(G) * S(A)$	$S_v(G) * S_v(A)$	$S_i(G) * S_i(A)$	$S_a(G) * S_a(A)$	Trapezoidal rule
0	0.0000	0.0000	0.0000	0.0000	0.0000	0.0000
τ	0.07032	0.160000	0.065498	0.066182	0.065936	0.080000
2τ	0.249329	0.427252	0.240400	0.245224	0.242008	0.267252
3τ	0.463732	0.606394	0.488636	0.431632	0.469928	0.446394
4τ	0.504273	0.566480	0.524040	0.489770	0.512812	0.486480
5τ	0.399577	0.379724	0.416770	0.395114	0.409682	0.379724
6τ	0.267844	0.254534	0.279370	0.264854	0.274620	0.254534
7τ	0.179542	0.170622	0.187268	0.177539	0.184082	0.170622

TABLE 2.6

EXAMPLE 2.4 RESPONSE FOR ($\tau = 2$)

t	$S(B)$ exact solution	$S(G) * S(A)$	$S_v(G) * S_v(A)$	$S_i(G) * S_i(A)$	$S_a(G) * S_a(A)$	Trapezoidal rule
0	0.0000	0.0000	0.0000	0.0000	0.0000	0.0000
τ	0.367879	0.0000	0.406870	0.133125	0.315622	0.0000
2τ	0.399577	0.533500	0.524460	0.295195	0.448039	0.533500
3τ	0.146996	0.115780	0.141628	0.195830	0.159695	0.115780
4τ	0.029305	0.019257	0.027805	0.039300	0.031636	0.019257

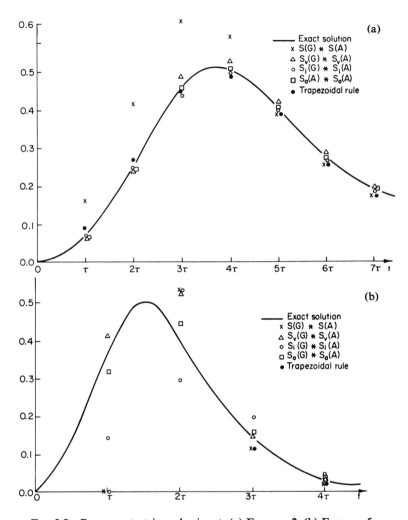

FIG. **2.8**   Response to triangular input. (a) For $\tau = 2$. (b) For $\tau = 5$.

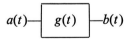

FIG. **2.9**   Transfer element. $a(t)$ is the input signal, $b(t)$ the output signal, and $g(t)$ the system impulse response.

For Example 2.4, $\tau = 1$ is one-half the smallest time constant, and the use of the intermediate area sequences with this relatively large increment size yields a maximum error of only 0.8 percent.

2.2.3 Other Superposition Integrals

Consider the linear system in Fig. 2.9.

In Laplace transform notation we have

$$B(s) = \mathcal{L}[a(t) * g(t)] = A(s)G(s), \qquad b(t) = \mathcal{L}^{-1}[B(s)]$$

where $\mathcal{L}[\ ]$ denotes the Laplace transform, $\mathcal{L}^{-1}[\ ]$ denotes the inverse transform, and $B(s)$, $A(s)$, and $G(s)$ are the Laplace transforms of $b(t)$, $a(t)$, and $g(t)$, respectively.

This convolution may also be written

$$b(t) = \mathcal{L}^{-1}[A(s)G(s)] = \mathcal{L}^{-1}\left[s^n A(s)\left(\frac{G(s)}{s^n}\right)\right]$$

for any integral n. In particular, for positive n,

$$\frac{G(s)}{s^n} = \mathcal{L}\left[\int_0^t \cdots \int_0^t g(t)(dt)^n\right] = \mathcal{L}\left[\int_0^t g(t)(dt)^n\right]$$

and

$$s^n A(s) = \mathcal{L}\left[\frac{d^n a(t)}{dt^n}\right] + \sum_{k=1}^n s^{n-k} \frac{d^{k-1}a(t)}{dt^{k-1}}\bigg|_{t=0+}$$

For the case $n = 1$, we have

$$a(t) * g(t) = \mathcal{L}^{-1}\left[sA(s)\frac{G(s)}{s}\right]$$

$$= \mathcal{L}^{-1}\left[\{\mathcal{L}[a'(t)] + a(0^+)\}\left\{\mathcal{L}\left[\int_0^t g(t)\,dt\right]\right\}\right]$$

$$= a'(t) * \int_0^t g(t)\,dt + a(0^+)\int_0^t g(t)\,dt$$

Since $g(t)$ is the impulse response of the system, we have the step response given by

$$\gamma(t) = \int_0^t g(t)\,dt$$

Thus

$$b(t) = a(t) * g(t) = a'(t) * \gamma(t) + a(0^+)\gamma(t)$$

If $a(0^-) = 0$, we have

$$b(t) = a(t) * g(t) = a'(t) * \gamma(t) + a(0^+)\gamma(t)$$

$$= \int_0^\infty a'(\tau)\gamma(t - \tau)\, d\tau + \int_{0-}^\infty a(0^+)\, \delta(\tau)\gamma(t - \tau)\, d\tau$$

$$= \int_{0-}^\infty [a'(\tau) + a(0^+)\, \delta(\tau)]\gamma(t - \tau)\, d\tau$$

$$= \int_{0-}^\infty a'(\tau)\gamma(t - \tau)\, d\tau = a'(t) * \gamma(t) \tag{2.7}$$

where $a'(t)$ is the generalized derivative of $a(t)$. That is, if $a(t)$ contains a step discontinuity of magnitude A at $t = t_0$, then $a'(t)$ contains an impulse of strength A at $t = t_0$ (see Bracewell [5]).

For example, suppose $a(t) = Ke^{-at}u(t)$; then

$$a'(t) = -Kae^{-at}u(t) + K\,\delta(t)$$

(see Fig. 2.10).

In practice, Eq. (2.7) is very useful, since physical system dynamics are often given in terms of the step response. Equation (2.7) may be interpreted as the superposition of the application of a succession of steps to the system. If the input function $a(t)$ is approximated by a sequence of steps (see Fig. 1.7(a)), we have

$$S_e(A) = [a_0{}^e, a_1{}^e, \ldots]$$

and the step response sequence

$$S(\gamma) = [\gamma_0, \gamma_1, \gamma_2, \ldots]$$

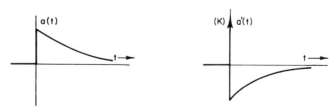

FIG. **2.10**   Generalized derivative.

Then

$$S(B) = S_e(A) * S(\gamma)$$

where $S(B)$ is the sequence of the response $b(t)$.

If the first derivative of $a(t)$ is approximated at $t = n\tau$ by

$$a'(n\tau) = \frac{a((n + \tfrac{1}{2})\tau) - a((n - \tfrac{1}{2})\tau)}{\tau} = \frac{a_{n+1}{}^v - a_n{}^v}{\tau}$$

then

$$S(A') = \frac{1}{\tau} S_v(A) * [1, -1]$$

$$= \frac{1}{\tau} [a_0{}^v, a_1{}^v - a_0{}^v, a_2{}^v - a_1{}^v, \ldots]$$

and clearly, from the definition of $S_e(A)$, we have

$$S_e(A) = S_v(A) * [1, -1] = [a_0{}^v, a_1{}^v - a_0{}^v, a_2{}^v - a_0{}^v, \ldots]$$

Thus

$$S_e(A) = \tau S(A') = S_v(A) * [1, -1]$$

In sequence notation, Eq. (2.7) becomes

$$S(B) = \tau S(A') * S(\gamma)$$

$$= \tau \left[\frac{1}{T} S_v(A) * [1, -1] \right] * S(\gamma)$$

$$= S_e(A) * S(\gamma) \tag{2.8}$$

as obtained above.

EXAMPLE 2.5

Consider the system and input of Example 2.4 (see Fig. 2.6). To determine the output sequence $S(B)$ for $\tau = 1$, we have

$$S_v(A) = [0.1, 0.3, 0.5, 0.7, 0.9, 0.9, 0.7, 0.5, 0.3, 0.1]$$
$$S(\gamma) = [0.00000, 0.18127, 0.32968, 0.45119, \ldots]$$

Since $g(t) = (1 - e^{-(t/5)})u(t)$,

$$S_e(A) = S_v(A) * [1, -1]$$
$$= [0.1, 0.2, 0.2, 0.2, 0.2, 0, -0.2, -0.2, -0.2, -0.2, -0.1]$$

TABLE 2.8

t	$S[B]$ exact solution	$S[B] = S[A] * S[G]$
0	0.000000	0.000000
1τ	0.187310	0.181270
2τ	0.703200	0.692220
3τ	1.488120	1.473090
4τ	2.493290	2.474950
5τ	3.678790	3.657740
6τ	4.637320	4.626130
7τ	5.059570	5.056440
8τ	5.042730	5.046200
9τ	4.666410	4.675280
10τ	3.995770	4.009060

The sequence $S(B) = S(\gamma) * S_e(A)$ appears in Table 2.8 along with the exact values. Comparison with Table 2.4 demonstrates that the accuracy of the convolution with the step response is comparable to that obtained with $S_a(A)$. In most cases the step response sequence is known; thus this method is both accurate and convenient. This procedure may be generalized to

$$b(t) = a(t) * g(t) = \mathscr{L}^{-1}\left[\frac{(S^l A(s))(S^k G(s))}{s^{l+k}}\right]$$

where l and k are integers and

$$b(t) = a(t) * g(t) = \int_{0-}^{t} a^{(l)}(t) g^{(k)}(t)(dt)^{l+k}$$

where

$$a^{(l)}(t) = \frac{d^l a(t)}{dt^l} \quad \text{and} \quad g^{(k)}(t) = \frac{d^k g(t)}{dt^k}$$

are generalized derivatives. This technique was first presented by Truxal [42].

EXAMPLE 2.6

To demonstrate the technique, we may consider a simple example with the $a(t)$ and $g(t)$ presented in Fig. 2.11. The time increment is large and $a(t)$ and $g(t)$ are piecewise linear. In practice, the time increment would be chosen significantly smaller for general $a(t)$ and $g(t)$.

This convolution is represented in Figs. 2.11 and 2.12. Figure 2.12 shows

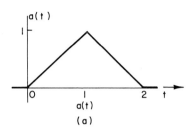
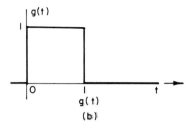

FIG. **2.11** Example 2.6.

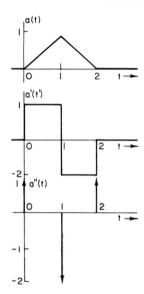
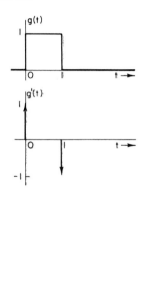

FIG. **2.12** Convolution example.

the two functions differentiated to yield sequences of impulses. For $\tau = 1$, the intermediate value sequence $S_i(A)$ and $S_i(G)$ are

$$S_i(A) = [0.5, 0.5]$$
$$S_i(G) = [1]$$

and the sequence $S(B)$:

$$S(B) = S_i(A) * S_i(G)D(-1)$$
$$= [0.5, 0.5] * [1] * [0, 1]$$
$$= [0, 0.5, 0.5]$$

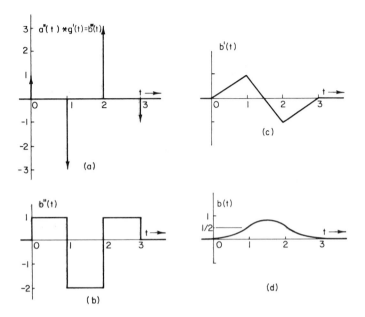

Fɪɢ. **2.13** Integration of convoluted impulses.

This result is also obtained by the generalized convolution integral. The procedure is presented pictorially in Figs. 2.12 and 2.13.

$$b(t) = a(t) * g(t) = \int_0^\infty a(\tau)g(t - \tau)\, d\tau$$

$$= \int_{0-}^t \int_{0-}^t \int_{0-}^t a''(t)g'(t)(dt)^3$$

The convolution of $a''(t) = [\delta(t) - 2\delta(t - 1) + \delta(t + 2)]$ with $g(t) = [\delta(t) - \delta(t - 1)]$ yields

$$
\begin{array}{rrrr}
1 & -2 & 1 & \\
1 & -1 & & \\
\hline
1 & -2 & 1 & \\
& -1 & 2 & -1 \\
\hline
1 & -3 & 3 & -1 \\
\end{array}
$$

$$a''(t) * g'(t) = \delta(t) - 3\delta(t - 1) + 3\delta(t - 2) - \delta(t - 3)$$

(See Fig. 2.13(a).)

This convolution is integrated three times, as presented in Fig. 2.13. The third integral (Fig. 2.13(d)) is the exact convolution $a(t) * g(t)$. For $\tau = 1$, we have the sequence

$$S(B) = [0, \tfrac{1}{2}, \tfrac{1}{2}, 0]$$

Clearly, for $\tau = 1/2$,

$$S(B) = [0, \tfrac{1}{8}, \tfrac{1}{2}, \tfrac{3}{4}, \tfrac{1}{2}, \tfrac{1}{8}, 0]$$

The result obtained with $\tau = 1$ is the same as that obtained with the use of the intermediate sequence. It is easy to show that if one function is piecewise linear and the other piecewise constant, these two methods always give the same result. However, if both are piecewise linear, the results in general will differ, as will be shown at the end of this section.

The notation may be simplified by the use of the z-transform. From Sec. 1.3, the z-transform of $u(t)$ and $tu(t)$ are

$$A_{u(t)}(z) = \frac{\tau z}{z - 1} \quad \text{and} \quad A_{tu(t)}(z) = \frac{\tau^2 z}{(z - 1)^2}$$

The operation $(1/s)A(s)$ corresponds in the time domain to $u(t) * a(t)$, in sequence notation to $\tau S(u) * S(A)$, and in z-transform notation to

$$\frac{\tau z}{z - 1} A(z)$$

Likewise, $(1/s^2)A(s)$ corresponds to

$$\frac{\tau^2 z}{(z - 1)^2} A(z)$$

In general we have the general relationship between the integrating operator $1/s^n$ and the z-transform:

$$\frac{1}{s^n} \longleftrightarrow \lim_{a \to 0} \frac{\tau(-1)^{n-1}}{(n-1)!} \left[\frac{2^{n-1}}{2a^{n-1}} \left(\frac{z}{z - e^{-at}} \right) \right] \tag{2.9}$$

The integrating operators for $n = 1 - 6$ are presented in Table 2.9.

The operation of integration is discussed in detail in Sec. 2.4, and several z-transform integrating operators are developed. For Example 2.6, we have

$$b(t) = a(t) * g(t)$$
$$s^3 B(s) = s^2 A(s) s G(s)$$
$$s^3 B(s) = \mathcal{L}[a''(t) * g'(t)]$$
$$= 1 - 3e^{-s} + 3e^{-2s} - e^{-3s}$$
$$B(s) = \frac{1}{s^3} [1 - 3e^{-s} + 3e^{-2s} - e^{-3s}]$$

TABLE 2.9

Laplace transform	Time function	z-transform
1	$\delta(t)$	1
$\dfrac{1}{s}$	$u(t)$	$\dfrac{\tau z}{z-1}$
$\dfrac{1}{s^2}$	$tu(t)$	$\dfrac{\tau^2 z}{(z-1)^2}$
$\dfrac{1}{s^2}$	$\dfrac{t^2}{2}u(t)$	$\dfrac{\tau^3}{2}\dfrac{z(z+1)}{(z-1)^3}$
$\dfrac{1}{s^4}$	$\dfrac{t^3}{6}u(t)$	$\dfrac{\tau^4}{6}\dfrac{z(z^2+4z+1)}{(z-1)^4}$
$\dfrac{1}{s^5}$	$\dfrac{t^4}{24}u(t)$	$\dfrac{\tau^5}{24}\dfrac{z(z^3+11z^2+11z+1)}{(z-1)^5}$
$\dfrac{1}{s^6}$	$\dfrac{t^5}{120}u(t)$	$\dfrac{\tau^6}{120}\dfrac{z(z^4+26z^3+66z^2+26z+1)}{(z-1)^6}$
$\dfrac{1}{s^m}$	$\dfrac{t^{m-1}}{(m-1)!}u(t)$	$\displaystyle\lim_{a\to 0}\dfrac{(-1)^{m-1}\tau}{(m-1)!}\left[\dfrac{\partial^{m-1}}{\partial a^{m-1}}\left(\dfrac{z}{z-e^{-a\tau}}\right)\right]$

For $\tau = 1$,

$$B(z) = \frac{1}{2}\frac{z(z+1)}{(z-1)^3}[1 - 3z^{-1} + 3z^{-2} - z^{-3}]$$

$$= \frac{1}{2}\frac{(z+1)}{z^2} = \frac{1}{2}[z^{-1} + z^{-2}]$$

which is the result obtained above. To obtain $b(z)$ directly from $A(z)$ and $G(z)$ (for arbitrary τ), we may take

$$B(s) = \frac{1}{s^3}[s^2 A(s)][sG(s)]$$

$$B(z) = \frac{\tau^3}{2}\frac{z(z+1)}{(z-1)^3}\left[\frac{(z-1)^2}{\tau^2 z}A(z)\right]\left[\frac{(z-1)}{\tau z}G(z)\right]$$

$$= \frac{z+1}{2z}A(z)G(z)$$

It is clear from Table 2.9 that in all cases $b(z)$ will be independent of the sample interval τ. Thus, for increased accuracy (to decrease τ), we need only change the sequences giving $A(z)$ and $G(z)$. For $\tau = 1/2$,

$$S(A) = [0, \tfrac{1}{2}, 1, \tfrac{1}{2}, 0]$$
$$S(G) = [1, 1, 0]$$
$$A(z) = \tfrac{1}{2}[\tfrac{1}{2}z^{-1} + z^{-2} + \tfrac{1}{2}z^{-3}]$$
$$G(z) = \tfrac{1}{2}[1 + z^{-1}]$$

$$B(z) = \frac{z+1}{2z}\left[\frac{1}{2}\left(\frac{1}{2}z^{-1} + z^{-2} + \frac{1}{2}z^{-3}\right)\right]\left[\frac{1}{2}(1 + z^{-1})\right]$$

$$B(z) = \frac{z^{-1}}{16}(1 + z^{-1})^4$$

$$B(z) = \frac{1}{16}[z^{-1} + 4z^{-2} + 6z^{-3} + 4z^{-4} + z^{-5}]$$

but

$$B(z) = \frac{1}{2}[b_0 + b_1 z^{-1} + b_2 z^{-2} + \cdots]$$

Thus the functional values of $b(t)$ at times $t = 0, \tfrac{1}{2}, 1, \ldots$ are

$$[0, \tfrac{1}{8}, \tfrac{1}{2}, \tfrac{3}{4}, \tfrac{1}{2}, \tfrac{1}{8}, 0]$$

which is, of course, the exact sequence.

For this example we have considered $a(t)$ and $g(t)$, which are polygonal in nature. If this is not the case, the functions may first be approximated by polygons, and thereafter the convolution is exact.

This method is particularly useful when differentiation of one of the functions reduces its sequence to a finite number of terms. This occurs when $a(t)$ asymptotically approaches a polynomial in t. In practice, the asymptotic polynomial is constant or linear. For example, if

$$S(A) = [0, 0.5, 0.7, 1, 2, 3, 4, 5, \ldots]$$

then $S(A) * [1, -1]^2$ has only a finite number of nonzero terms.

This z-transform technique may be compared with those presented in Secs. 2.2.1 and 2.2.2 by considering the increment of the convolution integral

$$B(k\tau) = \int_0^{k\tau} a_a(x) g_a(k\tau - x)\, dx$$

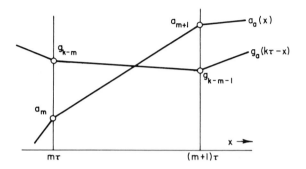

FIG. **2.14**   Convolution of linear approximations.

from $x = m\tau$ to $x = (m + 1)\tau$ as presented in Fig. 2.14. $a_a(x)$ and $g_a(k - x)$ are piecewise linear.

The contribution to the integral in this interval (for $g(k\tau - x)$ and $a(x)$ linear in the interval) is

$$\int_{m\tau}^{(m + 1)\tau} a_a(x)g_a(k\tau - x)\, dx$$

$$= \frac{\tau}{6}\,[a_m g_{k - m - 1} + 2a_m g_{k - m} + 2a_{m + 1}g_{k - m - 1} + a_{m + 1}g_{k - m}]$$

which may be easily verified by Simpson's rule.

Using the intermediate sequences (S_v, S_i, S_a) yields (for this interval)

$$\tau S_i(A) * S_i(G) = \frac{\tau}{4}\,[a_m g_{k - m - 1} + a_m g_{k - m} + a_{m + 1}g_{k - m - 1} + a_{m + 1}g_{k - m}]$$

and the sequences $S(A)$ and $S(G)$ yield (for this interval)

$$\tau S(A) * S(G) = \frac{\tau}{2}\,[a_m g_{k - m} + a_{m + 1}g_{k - m - 1}]$$

The exact value of the integral obtained by the z-transform technique is equal to the weighted average:

$$\int_{m\tau}^{(m + 1)\tau} a_a(x)g_a(k\tau - x)\, dx = \frac{\tau}{3}\,[2S_i(A) * S_i(G) + S(A) * S(G)]$$

Thus, in general, the z-transform technique and the use of the intermediate sequences do not yield the same results. The use of the intermediate sequences is easier to implement than the z-transform technique. In practice, the sequence convolution of Eq. (2.7) is most easily implemented, since the step response is more easily obtained from physical systems than is the impulse response. A similar procedure could, of course, be developed by using the ramp response.

2.2.4 The Convolution of Discontinuous Functions

Frequently both or one of the functions to be convolved (say $f(t)$ and $g(t)$) are discontinuous. When this is the case, the greatest accuracy is obtained by first writing $f(t)$ and $g(t)$, each as the sum of a continuous function and a piecewise constant function. In particular, suppose $f(t) = e^{-at}u(t)$; we write

$$f(t) = f_1(t) + f_2(t)$$

where

$$f_1(t) = u(t) \qquad \text{and} \qquad f_2(t) = (e^{-at} - 1)u(t)$$

Note that $f_2(t)$ is continuous and $f_1(t)$ is piecewise constant. If we also write

$$g(t) = g_1(t) + g_2(t)$$

where $g_1(t)$ and $g_2(t)$ satisfy the same conditions of $f_1(t)$ and $f_2(t)$, then

$$f(t) * g(t) = [f_1(t) + f_2(t)] * [g_1(t) + g_2(t)]$$
$$= f_1(t) * g_1(t) + f_1(t) * g_2(t) + f_2(t) * g_1(t) + f_2(t) + g_2(t)$$

For simplicity of the discussion we shall assume that $g(t)$ is continuous and $f(t)$ has a discontinuity only at $t = 0$. For additional discontinuities in either $f(t)$ or $g(t)$, the treatment is the same. With this assumption we have

$$f(t) * g(t) = f_1(t) * g(t) + f_2(t) * g(t)$$
$$= f(0^+) \int_0^t g(t)\, dt + f_2(t) * g(t)$$
$$= f_2(t) * g(t) + f(0^+)\gamma(t) \qquad (2.10)$$

The convolution $f_2(t) * g(t)$ may be performed by any convolution technique.

EXAMPLE 2.7

Suppose it is desired to perform the convolution $f(t) * g(t)$ when $f(t) = g(t) = e^{-t}u(t)$. This example, of course, allows comparison with the exact result, $te^{-t}u(t)$.

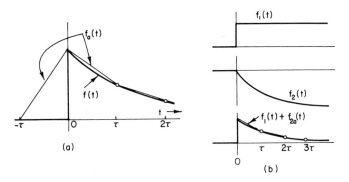

FIG. **2.15** Convolution of discontinuous functions. (a) Poor approximation. (b) Better approximation.

Using the z-transform technique of the Sec. 2.2.2, we obtain the exact convolution $f_a(t) * f_a(t)$, where $f_a(t)$ is the approximation of $f(t)$ by linear segments, shown in Fig. 2.15 (assuming a full sample at $t = 0$). Taking $f(t) = f_1(t) + f_2(t)$, where $f_1(t) = u(t)$ and $f_2(t) = (e^{-t} - 1)u(t)$, we may make the approximation shown in Fig. 2.15(b):

$$f(t) * g(t) = f(t) * f(t) = f_1(t) * f_1(t) + 2f_1(t) * f_2(t) + f_2(t) * f_2(t)$$
$$= F_{11}(t) + 2F_{12}(t) + F_{22}(t)$$

$$F_1(z) = Z[f_1(t)] = \frac{\tau z}{z - 1}$$

$$F_2(z) = \tau[f_2(0) + f_2(\tau)z^{-1} + f_2(2\tau)z^{-2} + \cdots + f_2(n\tau)z^{-n} + \cdots]$$

From Table 2.9 we have

$$F_{11}(z) = \left[F_1(z)\frac{z - 1}{\tau z}\right]\left[F_1(z)\frac{z - 1}{\tau z}\right]\left[\frac{\tau^2 z}{(z - 1)^2}\right] = \frac{\tau^2 z}{(z - 1)^2}$$

$$F_{11}(z) = \tau \sum_{n=0}^{\infty} (n\tau)z^{-n}$$

Thus

$$F_{11}(n\tau) = n\tau \quad \text{or} \quad S(F_{11}) = \tau[0, 1, 2, 3, 4, \ldots]$$

which is, of course, $u(t) * u(t)$.

Again from Table 2.9, we have

$$F_{12}(z) = \left[F_2(z)\frac{(z - 1)^2}{\tau^2 z}\right]\left[F_1(z)\frac{z - 1}{\tau z}\right]\left[\frac{\tau^3}{2}\frac{z(z + 1)}{(z - 1)^3}\right] = \frac{\tau}{2}\frac{z + 1}{z - 1}F_2(z)$$

Thus

$$S(F_{12}) = \frac{\tau}{2} S(F_2) * [1, 2, 3, \ldots]$$

$$= \frac{\tau}{2} [f_2(0), 2f_2(0) + f_2(\tau), \ldots]$$

and finally

$$F_{22}(z) = \left[F_2(z) \frac{(z-1)^2}{\tau^2 z} \right] \left[F_2(z) \frac{(z-1)^2}{\tau^2 z} \right] \left[\frac{\tau^4 z(z^2 + 4z + 1)}{6(z-1)^4} \right]$$

$$= \frac{1}{6} F_2(z)F_2(z)(z + 4 + z^{-1})$$

$$= \frac{1}{6} [F_2(z)z][F_2(z)][1 + 4z^{-1} + z^{-2}]$$

Thus

$$S(F_{22}) = \frac{\tau}{6} [f_2(\tau), f_2(2\tau), \ldots] * [f_2(0), f_2(\tau), \ldots] * [1, 4, 1]$$

$$= \frac{\tau}{6} [f_2(\tau)f_2(0), \ldots]$$

It is always possible to obtain the sequence $S(F_2)D(+1)$ corresponding to $[zF_2(z)]$, since $f_2(0) = 0$ by the construction of a continuous $f_2(t)$. For $\tau = 0.2$,

$$S(F * G) = S(F_{11}) + 2S(F_{12}) + S(F_{22})$$
$$= [0.0, 0.165, 0.270, 0.331, 0.362, 0.370, 0.364, \ldots]$$

which is compared with the actual values of $te^{-at}u(t)$ in Table 2.10 and Fig. 2.16.

TABLE 2.10

EXACT SOLUTION APPROXIMATION ($e^{-t}u(t) * e^{-t}u(t)$)

te^{-t}	$f(t) * f(t)$	te^{-t}	$f(t) * f(t)$
0.000000	0.000000	0.361428	0.363851
0.163746	0.1648412	0.345240	0.347553
0.268120	0.269921	0.323040	0.325219
0.329286	0.331487	0.297540	0.299494
0.359464	0.361852	0.270680	0.272559
0.367880	0.370338		

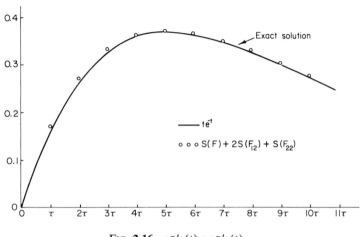

FIG. **2.16** $e^{-t}u(t) * e^{-t}u(t)$.

2.3 DECONVOLUTION

Deconvolution is the inverse of the "convolution" operation. When the input and the output of the transfer element are known, deconvolution enables determination of the transfer characteristic; in other words, the impulse or step response of this element.

2.3.1 The Deconvolution Operation

Given $b(t)$ and $a(t)$, deconvolution is the process of determining $g(t)$, where $b(t) = g(t) * a(t)$. For example, given the input and output data of a linear system, determine the impulse response. In sequence notation we write

$$S(B) = S(G) * S(A)$$
$$S(G) = S(B) \overset{*}{*} S(A)$$
$$S(G) = \frac{S(B)}{S(A)}$$

and the respective E- and z-transforms are written

$$G(E) = B(E):A(E)$$
$$G(z) = B(z):A(z)$$

The deconvolution of two sequences may be carried out by the following algorithm to determine

$$S(G) = \frac{S(B)}{S(A)}$$

$$
\begin{array}{cccc}
b_0 & b_1 & b_2 & \cdots \\[2mm]
b_0 & \dfrac{b_0}{a_0} b_1 & \dfrac{b_0}{a_0} a_2 & \cdots \\[2mm]
\hline
b_1 - b_0 \dfrac{a_1}{a_0} & b_2 - b_0 \dfrac{a_2}{a_0} & \cdots \\[2mm]
& \dfrac{a_1}{a_0}\left(b_1 - b_0 \dfrac{a_1}{a_2}\right) & \cdots \\[2mm]
\hline
& b_2 - b_0 \dfrac{a_2}{a_0} - \dfrac{a_1}{a_0}\left(b_1 - b_0 \dfrac{a_1}{a_2}\right) & \cdots
\end{array}
$$

$$S(G) = \left|\begin{array}{ccc} a_0 & a_1 & \cdots \\ \hline \dfrac{b_0}{a_0}, & \dfrac{1}{a_0}\left(b_1 - b_0 \dfrac{a_1}{a_0}\right), & \cdots \end{array}\right.$$

Thus

$$S(G) = [g_0, g_1, g_2, \ldots]$$

where

$$g_0 = \frac{b_0}{a_0} \qquad g_1 = \frac{1}{a_0}(b_1 - a_1 g_0) \qquad \cdots \qquad g_n = \frac{1}{a_0}\left(b_n - \sum_{r=1}^{n} a_k g_{n-k}\right) \quad (2.11)$$

EXAMPLE 2.8

Consider the system (integrator) with step response $b(t) = tu(t)$; taking $\tau = 1$, we have

$$S(G) = \frac{S(B)}{S(A)}$$

$$
\begin{array}{lll}
S(B) = 1 \quad 2 \quad 3 \quad 4 \quad \cdots & \qquad & S(A) = |1 \quad 1 \quad 1 \quad 1 \\
 1 \quad 1 \quad 1 \quad 1 & & S(G) = |1 \quad 1 \quad 1 \quad 1 \quad \cdots \\
\hline
 1 \quad 2 \quad 3 \quad \cdots \\
 1 \quad 1 \quad 1 \\
\hline
 1 \quad 2 \quad \cdots
\end{array}
$$

and, of course, we obtain the impulse response of the integrator $[1, 1, 1, \ldots]$.

EXAMPLE 2.9

In Example 2.2 it was shown that

$$[1, 2, 3, 1] * [1, 2, 1] = [1, 4, 8, 9, 5, 1]$$

It may be demonstrated by this algorithm that

$$[1, 4, 8, 9, 5, 1] \overset{*}{*} [1, 2, 3, 1] = [1, 2, 1]$$

and

$$[1, 4, 8, 9, 5, 1] \overset{*}{*} [1, 2, 1] = [1, 2, 3, 1]$$

It is always possible to divide the sequences $S(B)$ and $S(A)$ by a_0, yielding a sequence $S(A)$ that has a first term $a_0' = 1$. Hereafter it will be assumed that this has been done.

The deconvolution of two sequences given by their E- or z-transforms is the ratio of the E- or z-polynomials. Usually the z-transform may be expressed in the form

$$g(z) = \frac{b_0 + b_1 z^{-1} + b_2 z^{-2} + \cdots + b_n z^{-n}}{1 + a_1 z^{-1} + a_2 z^{-2} + \cdots + a_m z^{-m}}$$

The general term of the sequence $S(g)$ is given by

$$G_n = b_n - \sum_{k=1}^{n} a_k g_{n-k}$$

This recursion relation corresponds to the following system of equations:

$$
\begin{aligned}
g_0 &= b_0 & &= b_0 - \Sigma_0 \\
g_1 &= b_1 - a_1 g_0 & &= b_1 - \Sigma_1 \\
g_2 &= b_2 - (a_1 g_1 + a_2 g_0) & &= b_2 - \Sigma_2 \\
g_3 &= b_3 - (a_1 g_2 + a_2 g_1 + a_3 g_0) & &= b_3 - \Sigma_3 \\
g_4 &= b_4 - (a_1 g_3 + a_2 g_2 + a_3 g_1 + a_4 g_0) & &= b_4 - \Sigma_4 \\
&\ \vdots \\
g_n &= b_n - \left(\sum_{k=1}^{n} a_k g_{n-k} \right) & &= b_n - \Sigma_n
\end{aligned}
$$

This system may be solved by the following algorithm:

n	g_n	b_n	a_1	a_2	a_3	a_4	a_5	$\cdots$
0	g_0	b_0	$g_0 a_1$	$g_0 a_2$	$g_0 a_3$	$g_0 a_4$	$g_0 a_5$	$\cdots$
1	g_1	b_1	Σ_1	$g_1 a_1$	$g_1 a_2$	$g_1 a_3$	$g_1 a_4$	$\cdots$
2	g_2	b_2		Σ_2	$g_2 a_1$	$g_2 a_2$	$g_2 a_3$	$\cdots$
3	g_3	b_3			Σ_3	$g_3 a_1$	$g_3 a_2$	$\cdots$
4	g_4	b_4				Σ_4	$g_4 a_1$	$\cdots$
5	g_5	b_5					Σ_5	
$\vdots$								

EXAMPLE 2.10

Consider the deconvolution

$$S(G) = \frac{[1, 4, 8, 9, 5, 1]}{[1, 2, 3, 1]} = \frac{[b_0, b_1, b_2, b_3, b_4]}{[1, a_1, a_2, a_3]}$$

n	g_n	b_n	$a_1 = 2$	$a_2 = 3$	$a_3 = 1$	$a_4 = 0$	$a_5 = 0$
0	$g_0 = b_0 = 1$	$b_0 = 1$	$g_0 a_1 = 2$	$g_0 a_2 = 3$	$g_0 a_3 = 1$	$g_0 a_4 = 0$	$g_0 a_5 = 0$
1	$g_1 = b_1 - \Sigma_1 = 2$	$b_1 = 4$	$\Sigma_1 = 2$	$g_1 a_1 = 4$	$g_1 a_2 = 6$	$g_1 a_3 = 2$	0
2	$g_2 = b_2 - \Sigma_2 = 1$	$b_2 = 8$		$\Sigma_2 = 7$	2	3	1
3	0	$b_3 = 9$			$\Sigma_3 = 9$	0	0
4	0	$b_4 = 5$				$\Sigma_4 = 5$	0
5	0	$b_5 = 1$					$\Sigma_6 = 1$

As in Example 2.9, we obtain

$$S(G) = [1, 2, 1]$$

The system of equations for the deconvolution

$$g_n = b_n - \sum_{k=1}^{n} a_k g_{n-k}$$

may be written in determinantal as

$$g_0 = |b_0|$$

$$g_1 = \begin{vmatrix} 1 & b_0 \\ a_1 & b_1 \end{vmatrix} = b_1 - b_0 a_1$$

$$g_2 = \begin{vmatrix} 1 & 0 & b_0 \\ a_1 & 1 & b_1 \\ a_2 & a_1 & b_2 \end{vmatrix} = b_2 - b_1 a_1 - b_0(a_2 - a_1)^2$$

$$g_3 = \begin{vmatrix} 1 & 0 & 0 & b_0 \\ a_1 & 1 & 0 & b_1 \\ a_2 & a_1 & 1 & b_2 \\ a_3 & a_2 & a_1 & b_3 \end{vmatrix} = \begin{vmatrix} 1 & 0 & b_1 \\ a_1 & 1 & b_2 \\ a_0 & a_1 & b_3 \end{vmatrix} - b_0 \begin{vmatrix} a_1 & 1 & 0 \\ a_2 & a_1 & 1 \\ a_3 & a_2 & a_1 \end{vmatrix}$$

and in general

$$g_n = \begin{vmatrix} 1 & 0 & 0 & \cdots & 0 & b_0 \\ a_1 & 1 & 0 & \cdots & 0 & b_1 \\ a_2 & a_1 & 1 & \cdots & 0 & b_2 \\ \vdots & \vdots & \vdots & & \vdots & \\ & & & & 1 & b_{n-1} \\ a_n & a_{n-1} & a_{n-2} & & a_1 & b_n \end{vmatrix}$$

The determinantal form is frequently useful for computation on a digital computer.

It was shown in Sec. 2.2.1 that the convolution operation $S(B) = \tau S(G) * S(A)$ may be written in matrix notation (for trapezoidal integration) as

$$S(B) = \tau S(G) A_a$$

where

$$A_a = \begin{bmatrix} \dfrac{a_0}{2} & \dfrac{a_1}{2} & \dfrac{a_2}{2} & \dfrac{a_3}{2} & \dfrac{a_4}{2} & \cdots \\[2mm] 0 & \dfrac{a_0}{2} & a_1 & a_2 & a_3 & \cdots \\[2mm] 0 & 0 & \dfrac{a_0}{2} & a_1 & a_2 & \cdots \\[2mm] 0 & 0 & 0 & \dfrac{a_0}{2} & a_1 & \cdots \\[2mm] \vdots & \vdots & \vdots & \vdots & \vdots & \end{bmatrix}$$

or

$$S(B) = \tau S(A)A_g$$

where

$$A_g = \begin{bmatrix} \dfrac{g_0}{2} & \dfrac{g_1}{2} & \dfrac{g_2}{2} & \cdots \\[2ex] 0 & \dfrac{g_0}{2} & g_1 & \cdots \\[2ex] 0 & 0 & \dfrac{g_0}{2} & \cdots \\[2ex] \vdots & \vdots & \vdots & \end{bmatrix}$$

If the matrices are truncated at, say, n terms and $a_0 \neq 0$, we have

$$S(A) = \frac{1}{\tau} S(B)A_g{}^{-1} \qquad \text{and} \qquad S(G) = \frac{1}{\tau} S(B)A_a{}^{-1}$$

which is equivalent to the deconvolution algorithm given above. Note that if $x_0 \neq 0$, A_x is nonsingular.

The matrix formulation of the convolution

$$R_{ab}(\theta) = \int_0^\infty R_{aa}(\theta - x)g(x)\,dx$$

presented in Sec. 2.2.1 may be used for the determination of $S(G)$ by

$$S(G) = \frac{1}{\tau} S(z)A_a{}^{-1}$$

where $S(z)$ and A_a are as defined in Sec. 2.2.1. Further details are presented in Sec. 5.4.4.

2.3.2 Stability of the Deconvolution

A linear sampled-data system is said to be stable if for every bounded input sequence $S(B)$ the output sequence $S(A)$ is bounded. The output sequence of an unstable system frequently becomes unbounded in an exponential or polynomial fashion. If the sequence terms alternate in sign, we shall say that the system has an oscillatory instability. Most books on sampled-data systems present techniques for determination of system stability when $G(z) = B(z)/A(z)$ may be expressed in closed form. Thus, for this closed form case, we shall outline only one procedure.

If the poles (finite in number) of $G(z)$ all lie inside the unit circle, then $G(z)$ is stable. Thus it is required to determine if $G(z)$ has poles outside the unit circle. To determine this, one procedure is to transform $G(z)$ by the bilateral transformation

$$w = \frac{z + 1}{z - 1}, \qquad z = \frac{w + 1}{w - 1}$$

For $z = x + iy$, $w = u + iv$, we have

$$w = \frac{x + iy + 1}{x + iy - 1} = \frac{x^2 + y^2 - 1}{(x - 1)^2 + y^2} - i\,\frac{2y}{(x - 1)^2 + y^2}$$

or

$$u = \text{Re }[w] = \frac{(x^2 + y^2) + 1}{(x - 1)^2 + y^2}$$

Thus, for $|z|^2 = (x^2 + y^2) > 1$, we have $u > 0$, and for $|z|^2 < 1$, we have $u < 0$; that is, the bilateral transformation maps the interior of the unit circle of the z-plane into the left half of the w-plane (see Fig. 2.17). Thus, to

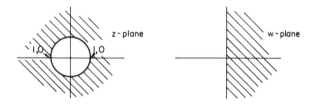

FIG. **2.17**   Bilateral transformation.

investigate the stability of $G(z)$ we need only determine if $G[(w + 1)/(w - 1)]$ has poles in the right half of the w-plane. This may be done by any of the standard root-determining criteria, such as the Hurwitz, Routh, and Leonhard criteria.

For example, suppose

$$S(G) = \frac{[1]}{[1, -1.6, 0.48]}$$

$$G(z) = \frac{1}{1 - 1.6z^{-1} + 0.48z^{-2}} = \frac{z^2}{z^2 - 1.6z + 0.48}$$

$$G\!\left(\frac{w + 1}{w - 1}\right) = \frac{w^2 + 2w + 1}{-0.12w^2 + 1.04w - 3.08}$$

All root-checking criteria show one root of the equation $[-0.12w^2 + 1.04w - 3.08 = 0]$ with positive real part, and $G(z)$, of course, has poles at

$$z = \frac{1.6 \pm \sqrt{0.54}}{2}$$

In practice, $G(z)$ is usually not known in closed form. Also we may have no control over $S(B)$. If $S(B)$ and $S(A)$ are given, perhaps from a record of past data, we may always perform the deconvolution outlined in Sec. 2.3.2. However, inaccuracies in the data due to measurement errors and/or a large sample interval may yield an unstable $S(G)$. If it is known that the system is stable, it is desirable to alter the data to eliminate the instability in the deconvolution. It has been the experience of these authors that the deconvolution is particularly sensitive to inaccuracies in the first few terms of $S(A)$.

If the terms of a sequence $S(A)$ become essentially constant, then the sequence $S(A) * [1, -1]$ may be expressed in closed form, since it contains only a finite number of nonzero terms. If this is true of $S(B)$ and $S(A)$, we may investigate the stability of $S(G)$ by taking

$$S(G) = \frac{S(B) * [1, -1]}{S(A) * [1, -1]}$$

Likewise, for $S(A) = [a_0, a_1, a_2, \ldots]$, where a_n becomes linear with increasing n, we have

$$S(A) * [1, -1] * [1, -1] = S(A) * [1, -1]^2$$

which contains only a finite number of nonzero terms. For example, consider

$$S(B) = k[0, 1, 2, 3, \ldots] \quad \text{and} \quad S(A) = [0, 1, 2, 3, \ldots]$$

(obviously $S(G) = k$).

We have

$$S(G) = \frac{k[0, 1, 2, 3, \ldots]}{[0, 1, 2, 3, \ldots]} = \frac{k[0, 1, 2, 3, \ldots] * [1, -1]^2}{[0, 1, 2, 3, \ldots] * [1, -1]^2}$$

or

$$S(G) = \frac{k[0, 1]}{[0, 1]}$$

$$G(z) = \tau \frac{kz^{-1}}{z^{-1}} = \tau k$$

EXAMPLE 2.11

The deconvolution technique has been applied to determine the transfer relationship between rainfall and water flow in a river [8].

This system is, of course, nonlinear, and any transfer relation will be a linearization. However, the step response (assuming linearity) obtained for different inputs (rainfall configurations) will be a measure of the nonlinearity of the system. If for all inputs the same step response results, it may be assumed that the system is linear.

Figure 2.18 presents the rainfall (on the area feeding the river) in cubic meters per second and the resultant flow. Curve 2 is that portion of the flow

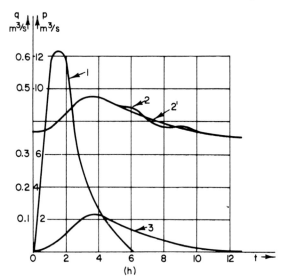

FIG. **2.18** Deconvolution, Example 2.11.

which is assumed to be the result of the rainfall of curve 1. The steady-state value of 0.36 m³/s has been subtracted out. This yields the sequence for the rainfall, $r(t)$, taking $t = 0$ at $t = 1$ hr in the figure.

$$S(R) = [10, 12, 6.1, 2.7, 0.7] \text{ m}^3/\text{s}$$

and the flow $f(t)$.

$$S(F) = [0.017, 0.064, 0.106, 0.111, 0.092, 0.071, 0.052, 0.035,$$
$$0.021, 0.011, 0.065, 0.002] \text{ m}^3/\text{s}$$

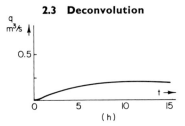

FIG. **2.19**   Step response.

The response to a step input of magnitude 10 m³/s is given by

$$S(\gamma) = \frac{S(F)}{S(R)} * 10[1, 1, 1, \ldots] = \frac{10S(F)}{S(R) * [1, -1]}$$

$$S(R) * [1, -1] = [10, 12, 6.1, 2.6, 0.7] * [1, -1]$$

$$= [10, 2, -5.9, -3.5, -1.9, -0.7]$$

$10S(F) =$				$S(R) * [1, -1] =$			
1.7	6.4	10.6	11.1	⋯	10	2	−5.9	−3.5	⋯
1.7	0.34	−1.003	−0.595	⋯				

$S(\gamma) =$			
0.17	0.606	1.039	⋯

0	6.06	11.603	11.625	⋯
	6.06	1.212	−3.575	⋯
0		10.391	15.270	⋯
		10.391	⋯
		0	⋯

This resultant sequence of the step response is presented in Fig. 2.19.

Figure 2.20 presents another record of rainfall and flow. For this case the deconvolution yields the step response shown as (2′) in Fig. 2.21. This deconvolution yields an instability that is known not to exist in the system.

For this case if we alter the input waveform slightly from curve 1 to the idealized curve 1′ and repeat the deconvolution to obtain the stable step response 2 in Fig. 2.21, curves 3 and 4 in the figure present the step response obtained from higher magnitude input rainfull. Obviously, the system is nonlinear, and as expected for larger amounts of rainfall, a greater percentage of the water reaches the river because seepage and evaporation are not proportional to volume of water.

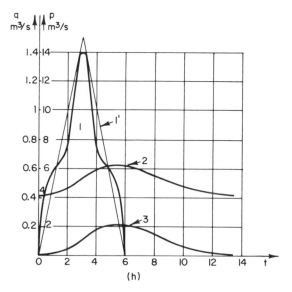

FIG. **2.20**   Deconvolution example.

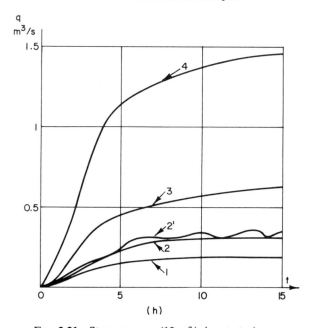

FIG. **2.21**   Step response (10 m³/s input step).

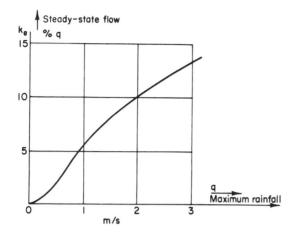

FIG. **2.22**   Steady-state flow to step input.

Figure 2.22 is a plot of the maximum (steady state) flow resulting from a step input of rainfall for different magnitudes of input, assuming that the input scale is the peak value of the input waveforms used for the deconvolution. This allows the calculation of the effect of rainfall on flood discharge.

Definite procedures have not been established for alteration of the sequence $S(B)$ to yield a stable deconvolution. When these procedures are established, the deconvolution will be a more valuable tool. Further research is, of course, encouraged along these lines.

Many other methods have been developed for stability discussion of the deconvolution operation. This question could be, by itself, the subject of a book, and the number of new publications in this field grows daily. The authors consider that the "try and see" procedure, which is sketched, has proved the most practical for computation with data given by input–output records.

2.3.3 Initial Value of the Deconvolution

For the linear system shown in Fig. 2.23 with the input signal $a(t)$, output signal $b(t)$, impulse response $g(t)$ and the step response,

$$\gamma(t) = \int_0^t g(t)\, dt$$

Since the output is given by the convolution

$$b(t) = a(t) * g(t) \qquad \text{or} \qquad S(B) = \tau S(A) * S(G)$$

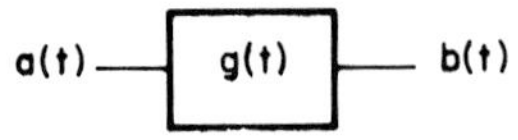

$$a(t) \longrightarrow \boxed{g(t)} \longrightarrow b(t)$$

FIG. **2.23**   Linear system.

we may determine the sequence representation of $g(t)$ by the deconvolution

$$S(G) = \frac{1}{\tau} \frac{S(B)}{S(A)}$$

Likewise (from Sec. 2.2.3) the step response sequence

$$S(\gamma) = \frac{S(B)}{S_e(A)}$$

In practice, the use of the deconvolution procedures outlined in Sec. 2.3.1 yield good results except for the first term. These inaccuracies in the first term of the deconvolution can be corrected by taking into consideration the input values a_1 and a_2 and the output values b_1 and b_2.

Consider the case where (for small t) the system input $a(t)$ is approximately linear $(a(t) \doteq (a_1/\tau)t)$, and the output $b(t)$ is approximately quadratic with zero intial slope $(a(t) \doteq (b_1/\tau^2)t^2)$. Then, using these approximations, we have the transfer function

$$G(S) = \frac{B(s)}{A(s)} = \frac{(b_1/\tau^2)(2/s^3)}{(a_1/\tau)(1/s^2)} = \frac{2b_1}{\tau a_1 s}$$

By the initial value theorem the first term of the sequence $S(G)$ is

$$g_0 = g(0) = \lim_{s \to \infty} \frac{2b_1}{\tau a_1} = \frac{2b_1}{\tau a_1} \tag{2.12}$$

For this deconvolution we replace the term $g_0 = b_1/\tau a_1$ $(a_0 = b_0 = 0)$ by the corrected term $g_0 = 2b_1/\tau a_1$. Table 2.11 presents revised values of the first term of the system impulse response and step response for the inputs and outputs shown in Fig. 2.24.

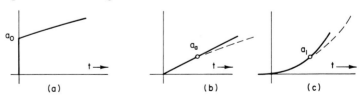

(a)   (b)   (c)

FIG. **2.24**   Small t approximation. (a) Step approximation. (b) Ramp. (c) Parabola.

TABLE 2.11

$$S(G) = \frac{1}{\tau}\frac{S(B)}{S(A)}, \quad \gamma t = \int_0^t g(t)\, dt$$

Input $a(t)$	Step	Output $b(t)$ Ramp	Parabola
Step	$g_0 = \infty$ $\gamma_0 = b_0/a_0$	$g_0 = b_1/\tau a_0$ $\gamma_0 = 0$	$g_0 = 0$ $\gamma_0 = 0$
Ramp	× × ×	$g_0 = \infty$ $\gamma_0 = b_1/a_1$	$g_0 = 2b_1/\tau a_1$ $\gamma_0 = 0$
Parabola	× × ×	× × ×	$g_0 = \infty$ $\gamma_0 = b_1/a_1$

EXAMPLE 2.12

Consider Example 2.4. For this system $g(t) = \frac{1}{5}e^{-(t/5)}$. Using the exact sequence of the output (from Table 2.4) and the exact input sequence (for $\tau = 1$)

$$S(a) = [0, 0.2, 0.4, 0.6, 0.8, 1.0, 0.8, 0.6, 0.4, 0.2]$$
$$S(b) = [0.0, 0.01873, 0.07032, 0.14881, 0.24933, \ldots]$$

and performing the deconvolution we have

$$S(G) = \frac{S(b)}{S(a)} = [0.093, 0.164, 0.135, 0.110, 0.090, \ldots]$$

which compares favorably with the exact sequence $S(G)$:

$$S(G) = [0.2, 0.164, 0.134, 0.109, 0.090, \ldots]$$

except for the first term. Table 2.12 compares this deconvolution (for $\tau = 1$) with the exact solution with the first term corrected by the above procedure to $g_0 = 2b_1/\tau a_1 = 0.1870$.

Greater accuracy can, of course, be obtained by choosing a smaller increment size. However, it is convenient to use as small an increment size as possible for the first-term calculation independent of the increment selection for the remainder of the operation. In this case ($g_0 = 2b_1/\tau a_1$) we have

τ	1	0.5	0.01
g_0	0.187	0.1936	0.199

For $\tau = 0.01$ (g_0 calculation only) we have g_0 correct to within 1 percent.

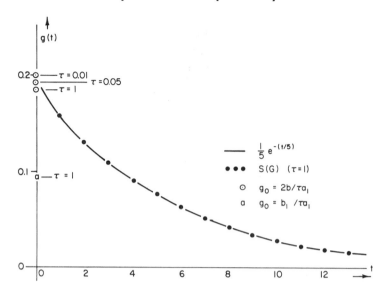

FIG. **2.25** Example 2.12.

The results of this deconvolution with the revised values of g are presented in Fig. 2.25.

TABLE 2.12

Example 2.12 ($\tau = 1$)

$S(G)$	Exact solution	$S(G)$	Exact solution
0.187000	0.200000	0.040510	0.040380
0.164290	0.163746	0.033170	0.033060
0.134515	0.134064	0.027160	0.027068
0.110125	0.109762	0.022235	0.022160
0.090165	0.089866	0.018210	0.018144
0.073825	0.073576	0.014895	0.014854
0.060440	0.060238	0.012200	0.012162
0.049485	0.049320		

2.4 INTEGRATION

By definition, each term of the intermediate area sequence $S_a(F)$ is the area

$$f_n{}^a = \int_{n\tau}^{(n+1)\tau} f(t)\, dt$$

Define:

$$I_k(t) = \int_0^t \cdots \int_0^t f(t)(dt)^k$$

The sequence representing $g_1(t) = \int_0^t f(t)\,dt$ is

$$S(I_1) = \tau\left[0, f_0{}^a, f_0{}^a + f_1{}^a, \ldots, \sum_{k=0}^{n-1} f_k{}^a, \ldots\right]$$

Thus

$$S(I_1) = \tau S_a(F) * [0, 1, 1, 1, \ldots] = \tau S_a(F) * [1, 1, 1, \ldots]D(-1)$$

Integration with the intermediate interpolating sequence $S_i(F)$ corresponding to the trapezoidal rule is given by the convolution

$$S(I_1) = \tau S_i(F) * [0, 1, 1, 1, \ldots] = \tau S_i(F) * [1, 1, 1, \ldots]D(-1)$$

Since

$$\tau\left[\frac{f_0 + f_1}{2}, \frac{f_1 + f_2}{2}, \frac{f_2 + f_3}{2}, \ldots\right] * [0, 1, 1, 1, \ldots]$$

$$= \tau\left[0, \ \frac{f_0 + f_1}{2}, \ \frac{f_0}{2} + f_1 + \frac{f_2}{2}, \ \frac{f_0}{2} + f_1 + f_2 + \frac{f_3}{2}, \ \ldots\right]$$

the trapezoidal rule in terms of $S(F)$ is

$$S(I_1) = \tau S(F) * \left[\frac{1}{2}, 1, 1, 1, \ldots\right] - \frac{\tau}{2}f_0[1, 1, 1, \ldots] \qquad (2.13)$$

Carrying out this convolution yields

	f_0	f_1	f_2	f_3
$\frac{1}{2}$	$\frac{f_0}{2}$	$\frac{f_1}{2}$	$\frac{f_2}{2}$	$\frac{f_3}{2}$
1		f_0	f_1	f_2
1			f_0	f_1
1				f_0
$\vdots$				

$$\frac{f_0}{2}, \ f_0 + \frac{f_1}{2}, \ f_0 + f_1 + \frac{f_2}{2}, \ f_0 + f_1 + f_2 + \frac{f_3}{2}, \ldots$$

$$-\left[\frac{f_0}{2}, \ \frac{f_0}{2}, \ \ \frac{f_0}{2}, \ \ \ \frac{f_0}{2}, \ldots\right]$$

$$S(I_1) = \tau\left[0, \ \frac{f_0}{2} + \frac{f_1}{2}, \ \frac{f_0}{2} + f_1 + \frac{f_2}{2}, \ \frac{f_0}{2} + f_1 + f_2 + \frac{f_3}{2}, \ \ldots\right]$$

EXAMPLE 2.13

It is easily verified that this trapezoidal integration of the functions $u(t)$ and $tu(t)$ yield the sequences

$$S\left(\int_0^t u(t)\, dt\right) = \tau[1, 1, 1, \ldots] * \left[\frac{1}{2}, 1, 1, 1, \ldots\right] - \frac{\tau}{2}[1, 1, 1, \ldots]$$

$$= \tau[0, 1, 2, 3, 4, \ldots]$$

$$S\left(\int_0^t t\, dt\right) = \tau\tau[0, 1, 2, 3, \ldots] * \left[\frac{1}{2}, 1, 1, 1, \ldots\right]$$

$$= \tau^2\left[0, \frac{1}{2}, \frac{4}{2}, \frac{9}{2}, \frac{16}{2}, \ldots, \frac{n^2}{2}, \ldots\right]$$

Repeated application of trapezoidal integration to the sequence $S(F)$ yields

$$S(I_2) = \left\{S(F) * \tau\left[\frac{1}{2}, 1, 1, \ldots\right] - \frac{\tau}{2}f_0[1, 1, 1, \ldots]\right\} * \tau\left[\frac{1}{2}, 1, 1, \ldots\right]$$

$$= S(F) * \tau^2\left[\frac{1}{2}, 1, 1, 1, \ldots\right]^2 - \frac{\tau^2}{2}f_0[1, 1, 1, \ldots] * \left[\frac{1}{2}, 1, 1, \ldots\right]$$

Since the initial value of $\int_0^t f(t)\, dt = 0$, in general for the kth integration we have

$$S(I_k) = S(F) * \tau^k\left(\frac{1}{2}, 1, 1, 1, \ldots\right)^k$$

$$- \frac{\tau^k}{2}f_0[1, 1, 1, \ldots] * \left[\frac{1}{2}, 1, 1, \ldots\right]^{k-1} \qquad (2.14)$$

where

$$I_k(t) = \int_0^t \cdots \int_0^t f(t)(dt)^k$$

Greater accuracy for higher-order integrals may be obtained by integrating with the step sequence $S_e(F)$. This method is based upon the superposition of the exact sequences of the high-order integral of the step functions.

For

$$S_e(F) = [f_0{}^e, f_1{}^e, f_2{}^e, \ldots]$$

where

$$f_n{}^e = f_n{}^a - f_{n-1}{}^a$$

we have

$$S_e(F) = S_a(F) * [1, -1]$$

Consider the integral of the function $S_e(F) = [1, 0, 0, \ldots]$, representing $f(t) = u(t)$. The exact sequence representation of $\int_0^t f(t)\, dt$ is

$$S\left(\int_0^t f(t)\, dt\right) = S\left(\int_0^t u(t)\, dt\right) = \tau[0, 1, 2, 3, \ldots]$$

and for $S_e(F)$ we have

$$S(I_1) = S_e(F) * \tau[0, 1, 2, 3, \ldots]$$

In general, for the kth integral,

$$S(I_k) = S_e(F) * \frac{\tau^k}{k!} [0, 1^k, 2^k, 3^k, \ldots]$$

$$= \frac{\tau^k}{k!} S_a(F) * [1, -1] * [0, 1^k, 2^k, 3^k, \ldots]$$

$$= \frac{\tau^k}{k!} S_a(F) * [0, 1^k, 2^k - 1^k, 3^k - 2^k, \ldots] \qquad (2.15)$$

In z-transform notation we have, for the z-transform of the kth integral,

$$I_k(z) = F(z) \frac{1}{\tau} [1 - z^{-1}] Z\left\{\frac{\tau^k}{k!} [0, 1^k, 2^k, 3^k, \ldots]\right\}$$

$$= F(z) \frac{1}{\tau} [1 - z^{-1}] Z\left\{\frac{1}{k!} [0, \tau^k, (2\tau)^k, (3\tau)^k, \ldots]\right\}$$

$$= F(z) \frac{1}{\tau} (1 - z^{-1}) Z\left\{\frac{t^k}{k!}\right\}$$

where $I_k(z)$ is the z-transform of $I_k(t)$.
  For $k = 1$ we have

$$I_1(z) = F(z) \frac{1}{T} (1 - z^{-1}) \frac{T^2 z}{(z-1)^2} = \frac{Tz^{-1}}{1 - z^{-1}} F(z)$$

$$= \left(\frac{T}{z-1}\right) F(z)$$

For $k = 2$,

$$I_2(z) = \left(\frac{1}{T}\frac{z-1}{z}\right)\frac{T^3}{2}\left(\frac{z(z+1)}{(z-1)^3}\right)F(z) = \left(\frac{T^2}{2}\frac{z+1}{(z-1)^2}\right)F(z)$$

For $k = 3$,

$$I_3(z) = \left(\frac{1}{T}\frac{z-1}{z}\right)\left(\frac{T^4}{6}\frac{z(z^2+4z+1)}{(z-1)^4}\right)F(z)$$

$$= \left(\frac{T^3}{6}\frac{(z^2+4z+1)}{(z-1)^3}\right)F(z)$$

For $k = 4$,

$$I_4(z) = \left(\frac{1}{T}\frac{z-1}{z}\right)\left(\frac{T^5}{24}\frac{z(z^3+11z^2+11z+1)}{(z-1)^5}\right)F(z)$$

$$= \left(\frac{T^4}{24}\frac{z^3+11z^2+11z+1}{(z-1)^4}\right)F(z)$$

Note that these integrating operators are obtained from Table 2.9 by taking

$$I_k(z) = \frac{Z\{1/s^{k+1}\}}{Z\{1/s\}}F(z)$$

In a similar fashion we may use the z-transform of the ramp sequence $S_r(F)$, as demonstrated in Sec. 2.2.3. From Table 2.9, we have

$$I_k(z) = \frac{Z\{1/s^{k+2}\}}{Z\{1/s^2\}}F(z)$$

This is the Madwed-Truxal [23, 42] integrating operator. Thus

$$I_1(z) = \frac{(z-1)^2}{T^2z}\frac{T^3}{2}\frac{z(z+1)}{(z-1)^3}F(z)$$

$$= \left(\frac{T}{2}\frac{z+1}{z-1}\right)F(z)$$

$$I_2(z) = \left(\frac{T^2}{6}\frac{z^2+4z+1}{(z-1)^2}\right)F(z)$$

$$I_3(z) = \left(\frac{T^3}{24}\frac{z^3+11z^2+11z+1}{(z-1)^3}\right)F(z)$$

$$I_4(z) = \left(\frac{T^4}{120}\frac{z^4+26z^3+66z^2+26z+1}{(z-1)^4}\right)F(z)$$

This form of substitutional z-transform integration may, of course, be extended to higher-order polynomial approximations. In general the integrating operator

$$H_k(z) = \frac{Z\{1/s^{k+n}\}}{Z\{1/s^n\}}$$

yields $I_k(z) = H_k(z)F(z)$, where $I_k(t)$ is exact when $f(t)$ has $n - 2$ continuous derivatives at the sample points and is an $(n - 1)$th-order polynomial in the interval. Suppose these conditions are satisfied for $f(t)$. Then the nth derivative of $f(t)$ is a sequence of (Dirac) impulses. Thus

$$Z\left\{\frac{1}{s^n}\right\}Z\left\{\frac{d^n f(t)}{dt^n}\right\} = F(z)$$

is exact, or

$$Z\left\{\frac{d^n f(t)}{dt^n}\right\} = \frac{F(z)}{Z\{1/s^n\}}$$

is the z-transform of a sequence of impulses that may be integrated $(k + n)$ times exactly by taking

$$I_k(z) = Z\left\{\frac{1}{s^{k+n}}\right\}Z\left\{\frac{d^n f(t)}{dt^n}\right\}$$

$$= \frac{Z\{1/s^{k+n}\}}{Z\{1/s^n\}}F(z)$$

which is the expression obtained above.

For example, taking $k = 1$ and $n = 2$, we have the Madwed-Truxal integrating operator [23, 42]

$$I_1(z) = \left(\frac{T}{2}\frac{z+1}{z-1}\right)F(z)$$

In sequence notation,

$$S(I_1) = \tau S(F) * [\tfrac{1}{2}, 1, 1, 1, \ldots]$$

which is, of course, exact for $f(t)$ continuous (zero-order derivative) at the sample points and linear (first-order polynomial) within the segments (this is the trapezoidal rule).

If $[df(t)/dt]$ is continuous at the sample points and $f(t)$ is a second-degree polynomial within the sample interval, then $(d^3 f(t)/dt^3)$ contains impulses only at the sample instants. Thus we have the exact relation for $k = 1$ and $n = 3$:

$$Z\left\{\frac{d^3f(t)}{dt^3}\right\} = \frac{1}{Z\{1/s^3\}} F(z)$$

which is the z-transform of a sequence of impulses.

Integrating these impulses four times yields

$$I_1(z) = Z\left\{\frac{1}{s^4}\right\}\left[\frac{1}{Z\{1/s^3\}} F(z)\right]$$

$$= \left(\frac{T^4}{6} \frac{z(z^2 + 4z + 1)}{(z - 1)^4}\right)\left(\frac{2}{T^3} \frac{(z - 1)^3}{z(z + 1)}\right)F(z)$$

$$= \frac{T}{3}\left(\frac{z^2 + 4z + 1}{z^2 - 1}\right)F(z)$$

which is Simpson's rule.†

Many z-transform substitutional integrators have appeared in the literature. Table 2.13 presents a tabulation of several of these methods and the appropriate references.

Regarding the sequence $S(F)$ as a row vector,

$$S(F) = [f_0, f_1, f_2, \ldots]$$

we may write the integrating operators in matrix notation. For example, for the trapezoidal rule, we have

$$S(F)\mathbf{B}_1 = \tau\left[0, \frac{f_0}{2} + \frac{f_1}{2}, \frac{f_0}{2} + f_1 + \frac{f_2}{2}, \ldots\right]$$

where

$$\mathbf{B}_1 = \tau\begin{bmatrix} 0 & 0.5 & 0.5 & 0.5 & \cdots \\ 0 & 0.5 & 1 & 1 & \cdots \\ 0 & 0 & 0.5 & 1 & \\ 0 & 0 & 0 & 0.5 & \\ \vdots & \vdots & \vdots & \vdots & \cdots \end{bmatrix}$$

---

† It is easy to verify that the integral over two intervals of the unique quadratic fitting the three points (Simpson's rule) is identical to the integral of the interpolation constructed by taking for the first interval an arbitrary quadratic fitting the first two points and the unique quadratic fitting the second two points and having continuous first derivative at the intermediate point for the second interval.

TABLE 2.13

SOME z-TRANSFORM INTEGRATORS

	$\dfrac{1}{s}$	$\dfrac{1}{s^2}$	$\dfrac{1}{s^3}$	$\dfrac{1}{s^4}$
First difference	$\left(\dfrac{\tau z}{z-1}\right)$	$\left(\dfrac{\tau z}{z-1}\right)^2$	$\left(\dfrac{\tau z}{z-1}\right)^3$	$\left(\dfrac{\tau z}{z-1}\right)^4$
z-transform	$\dfrac{\tau z}{z-1}$	$\dfrac{\tau^2 z}{(z-1)^2}$	$\dfrac{\tau^3}{2}\dfrac{z(z+1)}{(z-1)^3}$	$\dfrac{\tau^4}{6}\dfrac{z(z^2+4z+1)}{(z-1)^4}$
Naslin [25]	$\dfrac{\tau}{2}\dfrac{z+1}{z-1}$	$\dfrac{\tau^2}{8}\dfrac{z^2+6z+1}{(z-1)^2}$	$\dfrac{\tau^3}{2}\dfrac{z(z+1)}{(z-1)^3}$	$\dfrac{\tau^4}{6}\dfrac{z(z^2+4z+1)}{(z-1)^4}$
Boxer–Thaler [4]	$\dfrac{\tau}{2}\dfrac{z+1}{z-1}$	$\dfrac{\tau^2}{12}\dfrac{z^2+10z+1}{(z-1)^2}$	$\dfrac{\tau^3}{2}\dfrac{z(z+1)}{(z-1)^3}$	$\dfrac{\tau^4}{6}\dfrac{z(z^2+4z+1)}{(z-1)^4}-\dfrac{\tau^4}{720}$
Tustin [45]	$\left(\dfrac{\tau}{2}\dfrac{z+1}{z-1}\right)$	$\left(\dfrac{\tau}{2}\dfrac{z+1}{z-1}\right)^2$	$\left(\dfrac{\tau}{2}\dfrac{z+1}{z-1}\right)^3$	$\left(\dfrac{\tau}{2}\dfrac{z+1}{z-1}\right)^4$
Halijak [16]	$\dfrac{\tau z}{z-1}$	$\dfrac{\tau^2 z}{(z-1)^2}$	$\dfrac{\tau^3}{2}\dfrac{z(z+1)}{(z-1)^3}$	$\dfrac{\tau^4}{4}\dfrac{z(z+1)^2}{(z-1)^3}$
Madwed–Truxal [23, 42]	$\dfrac{\tau}{2}\dfrac{z+1}{z-1}$	$\dfrac{\tau^2}{6}\dfrac{z^2+4z+1}{(z-1)^2}$	$\dfrac{\tau^3}{24}\dfrac{z^3+11z^2+11z+1}{(z-1)^3}$	$\dfrac{\tau^4}{24}\dfrac{z^4+26z^3+66z^2+26z+1}{(z-1)^4}$
General	$\dfrac{Z\{1/s^{k+1}\}}{Z\{1/s^k\}}$	$\dfrac{Z\{1/s^{k+2}\}}{Z\{1/s^k\}}$	$\dfrac{Z\{1/s^{k+3}\}}{Z\{1/s^k\}}$	$\dfrac{Z\{1/s^{k+4}\}}{Z\{1/s^k\}}$

For Simpson's 1/3 rule we have

$$
\mathbf{B}_2 = \frac{\tau}{6}
\begin{bmatrix}
0 & 3 & 2 & 2 & 2 & 2 & \cdots \\
0 & 3 & 8 & 8 & 8 & 8 \\
0 & 0 & 2 & 5 & 4 & 4 \\
0 & 0 & 0 & 3 & 8 & 8 \\
0 & 0 & 0 & 0 & 2 & 5 \\
0 & 0 & 0 & 0 & 0 & 3 \\
\vdots & \vdots & \vdots & \vdots & \vdots & \vdots & \cdots
\end{bmatrix}
$$

When an odd number of intervals is included in the integration (odd-numbered colums), the last interval is integrated by the trapezoidal rule.

In a similar fashion we obtain, using third-order polynomials,

$$
\mathbf{B}_3 = \frac{\tau}{4}
\begin{bmatrix}
0 & 12 & 8 & 9 & 8 & 8 & 8 & 8 & 8 & \cdots \\
0 & 12 & 32 & 27 & 32 & 32 & 32 & 32 & 32 \\
0 & 0 & 8 & 27 & 16 & 17 & 16 & 16 & 16 \\
\vdots & & 0 & 9 & 32 & 27 & 32 & 32 & 32 \\
& & & 0 & 8 & 27 & 16 & 17 & 16 \\
& & & & 0 & 9 & 32 & 27 & 32 \\
& & & & & 0 & 8 & 27 & 16 \\
& & & & & & 0 & 9 & 32 \\
& & & & & & & 0 & 0 \\
& & & & & & & & 0 \\
& & & & & & & & 0 & \cdots
\end{bmatrix}
$$

Several higher-order integrating rules using matrix notation are presented by Ronveaux [35].

These matrices may, of course, be entered permanently into a computer and called when required.

To perform higher-order integration, say $g_k(t)$, we need only take

$$S(G_k) = S(F)\mathbf{B}^k$$

2.5 DIFFERENTIATION

It was demonstrated in Sec. 2.2.3 that a sequence representation of the first derivative is given by the difference between two adjacent terms of the intermediate value sequence divided by the unit interval τ. This representation

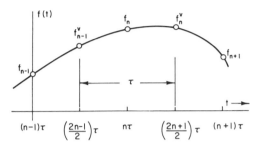

FIG. **2.26** Central difference.

corresponds to the *central difference* approximation to the derivative. (See Fig. 2.26.) Thus

$$g(n\tau) = \frac{df(t)}{dt}\bigg|_{t=n\tau} = f_n' \approx \frac{f_n^v - f_{n-1}^v}{\tau}$$

Thus

$$S(G) = S\left(\frac{df}{dt}\right) = \frac{1}{\tau} S_v(F) * [1, -1]$$

where $S_v(F)$ is the intermediate value sequence of the function $f(t)$.

If $S_v(F)$ is replaced by $S_i(F)$ (which is exact for piecewise linear $f(t)$), we have (except for the first term)

$$S(G) = \frac{1}{2\tau} [(S(F) * [1, 1])D(+1)] * [1, -1]$$

$$S\left(\frac{df}{dt}\right) = \frac{1}{2\tau} [S(F) * [1, 0, -1]D(+1)] \qquad (2.16)$$

Since

$$S_i(F) = \tfrac{1}{2}[S(F) * [1, 1]]D(+1)$$

which is the central difference taken with an interval 2τ about the point $t = n\tau$.

The approximate derivative

$$S\left(\frac{df}{dt}\right) = \frac{1}{\tau} S_v(F) * [1, -1] \qquad (2.17)$$

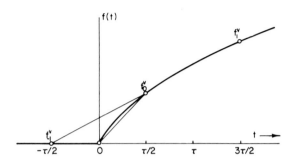

FIG. **2.27**   First term adjustment.

is a reasonable approximation except for the first term. For the first term
this sequence yields

$$g_0 = \frac{f_0^v - f_{-1}^v}{\tau} = \frac{f_0^v}{\tau}$$

Figure 2.27 demonstrates that the *forward difference*

$$g_0 = \frac{f_0^v}{\tau/2} = \frac{2f_0^v}{\tau}$$

is more accurate. With this adjustment of the first term we have

$$S\left(\frac{df}{dt}\right) = S(F') = \frac{1}{\tau} S_v(F) * [1, -1] + \left[\frac{f_0^v}{\tau}, 0, 0, \ldots\right]$$

$$= \frac{1}{\tau} S_v(F) * [1, -1] + \left[\frac{f_0^v}{\tau}\right]$$

The first term of the sequence,

$$S\left(\frac{df}{dt}\right) = \frac{1}{2\tau} [S(F) * [1, 0, -1]]D(+1)$$

must be adjusted in a similar manner to obtain

$$S\left(\frac{df}{dt}\right) = \frac{1}{2\tau} [S(F) * [1, 0, -1]]D(+1) + \left[\frac{f_1 - 2f_0}{2\tau}\right]$$

Clearly, this adjustment yields inferior results for the first term if the
function is similar to that depicted in Fig. 2.28.

Thus it is desirable to adopt a more accurate estimate of the first term.
If, at the time the calculation of g_0 is required, f_0^v and f_1^v are known (this is,
of course, not necessarily true in a real time process), the first term of $S(G)$

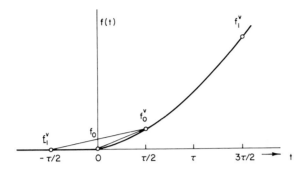

FIG. **2.28** First term adjustment.

may be evaluated by fitting a quadratic to the points $(f_0, 0)$, $(f_0^v, \tau/2)$, and $(f_1^v, 3\tau/2)$, yielding for $f_0 = 0$:

$$\frac{df}{dt}\bigg|_{t=0} = g_0 = \frac{1}{\tau}\left[3f_0^v - \frac{1}{3}f_1^v\right]$$

This is easily verified and is left as an exercise for the reader.

With this adjustment, we have

$$S\left(\frac{df}{dt}\right) = S(G) = \frac{1}{\tau}S_v(F) * [1, -1] + \frac{1}{\tau}\left[2f_0^v - \frac{1}{3}f_1^v\right]$$

The sequence involving $S(F)$ may be adjusted in a similar fashion by fitting a quadratic to the points $(0, 0)$, (f_1, τ) and $(f_2, 2\tau)$ to obtain

$$S(G) = \frac{1}{2\tau}[S(F) * [1, 0, -1]]D(+1) + \left[\frac{3f_1 - f_2}{2\tau}\right]$$

This expression is in fact the sequence (with general term g_n) obtained by approximating $f(t)$ by a quadratic fitting the points $[f_{n-1}, (n-1)\tau]$, $[f_n, n\tau]$, and $[f_{n+1}, (n+1)\tau]$. Verification of this is left as an exercise for the reader.

EXAMPLE 2.14

Consider $f(t) = (t^2/2)u(t)$.

For $\tau = 1$,

$$S_v(F) = [0.125, 1.125, 3.125, 6.125, 10.125, 15.125, \ldots]$$

$$S(G) = \frac{1}{\tau}S_v(F) * [1, -1] + \frac{1}{\tau}\left[2f_0^v - \frac{1}{3}f_1^v\right]$$

$$= [0.125, 1.0, 2.0, 3.0, 4.0, \ldots] + [-0.125]$$

$$= [0, 1.0, 2.0, 3.0, 4.0, \ldots]$$

which is, of course, the sequence corresponding to $f'(t) = tu(t)$. Also,

$$S(F) = [0.0, 0.5, 2.0, 4.5, 8.0, 12.5, \ldots]$$

$$S(G) = \frac{1}{2\tau}[S(F) * [1, 0, -1]]D(+1) + \left[\frac{3f_1 - f_2}{2\tau}\right]$$

$$= [0.25, 1.0, 2.0, 3.0, 4.0, \ldots] + [-0.25]$$

$$= [0, 1.0, 2.0, 3.0, 4.0, \ldots]$$

It is easily verified that the backward difference sequence $S_B(G)$ and the forward difference $S_F(G)$ are given by

$$S_B(G) = \frac{1}{\tau} S(F) * [1, -1]$$

and

$$S_F(G) = \frac{1}{\tau}[S(F) * [1, -1]]D(+1)$$

The generalized integrating operators yield good results if the function being integrated is reasonably well behaved. That is, the function may be accurately approximated by polynomials. These generalized integrating operators are also valid for differentiation. For example, to take the first derivative of a function $f(t)$, which is piecewise linear, we may take

$$F'(z) = \left[\frac{(z-1)^2}{T^2 z} F(z)\right]\left[\frac{Tz}{z-1}\right]$$

which is the forward difference. The term in the first brackets is the z-transform of a sequence of impulses (the second derivative of $f(t)$). Integrating once (second term) yields the exact z-transform of $f'(t)$.

Thus the z-transforms of Table 2.9 or 2.13 may be used in the expression

$$Z(f^{(n)}(t))F(z)\left[\frac{Z\{1/s^{k-n}\}}{Z\{1/s^k\}}\right]$$

to yield the z-transform of the nth derivative. This representation is exact if $f(t)$ is a $(k-1)$th-degree polynomial in each interval with a continuous $(k-2)$th derivative at the sample points.

EXAMPLE 2.15

$$f(t) = \frac{t^2}{2} u(t)$$

$$F(z) = \frac{T^3}{2} \frac{z(z+1)}{(z-1)^3}$$

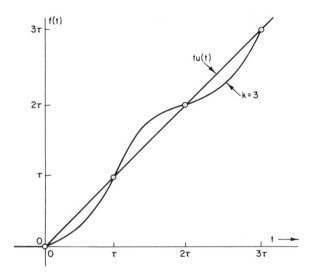

FIG. **2.29** $tu(t)$ and approximations.

Take $k = 3, n = 1$:

$$Z\{f'(t)\} = \frac{T^3}{2} \frac{z(z+1)}{(z-1)^3} \left[\frac{2}{T^3} \frac{(z-1)^3}{z(z+1)} \frac{T^2 z}{(z-1)^2} \right] = \frac{T^2 z}{(z-1)^2}$$

which is, of course, the z-transform of

$$f'(t) = tu(t)$$

Great care must be exercised in the use of the z-transform method in that (except in special cases) we usually choose $k = 2$. This, of course, corresponds to the first difference formulation of the derivative. To demonstrate the problem, consider the function $tu(t)$ in Fig. 2.29. The approximation for $k = 2$ is exact. However, for $k = 3$, we have a poor approximation.

For $k = 2$ we have

$$G(z) = \left[\frac{Tz}{z-1} \right] \left[\frac{(z-1)^2}{T^2 z} \right] F(z) = \frac{1}{T} [z-1] F(z)$$

$$= \frac{1}{T} [z-1] \left[\frac{T^2 z}{(z-1)^2} \right] = \frac{Tz}{z-1}$$

or

$$S(G) = [1, 1, 1, 1, \ldots]$$

For $k = 3$ we have

$$G(z) = \left[\frac{2}{T^3}\frac{(z-1)^2}{z(z+1)}\right]\left[\frac{T^2z}{(z-1)^2}\right]F(z)$$

$$= \left(\frac{2}{T}\left[\frac{z-1}{z+1}\right]\right)\frac{T^2z}{(z-1)^2} = \frac{2Tz}{(z+1)(z-1)} = \frac{2Tz}{z^2-1}$$

or

$$S(G) = [0, 2, 0, 2, 0, 2, \ldots]$$

as in Fig. 2.29.
For $k = 4$ we have

$$S(G) = [0, 1, -2, 9, -32, \ldots]$$

Approximations to higher-order derivatives may be obtained by repeated application of the procedures given above. However, inaccuracies in the data due to noise and sampling are amplified by differentiation. Thus, except in special cases, it is difficult to obtain a reasonable estimate of any deriva-

TABLE 2.14

SURVEY OF SOME FUNCTIONAL OPERATIONS WITH IMPULSE ANALYSIS AND
LAPLACE TRANSFORM

Operation	Analytical expression	Impulse analysis	Laplace transform calculus
Addition and subtraction	$f(t) \pm g(t)$	$S(F) \pm S(G)$	$F(s) \pm G(s)$
Convolution	$\int_0^t f(t-\theta)g(\theta)\,d\theta$	$S(F) * S(G)$	$F(s) \cdot G(s)$
Deconvolution		$S(F) \overset{*}{*} S(G)$	$F(s):G(s)$
Integration	$\int_0^t f(t)\,dt$	$S(F) \overset{*}{*} \frac{1}{\tau}[1, -1]$	$F(s):s$
Differentiation	df/dt	$S(F) * \frac{1}{\tau}[1, -1]$	$F(s) - f_0$
Unit impulse	$\delta(t)$	$[1]$	1
Differentiation of the unit impulse		$\frac{1}{\tau}[1, -1]$	s
Step function	$u(t)$	$[1] \overset{*}{*} [1, -1]$	$1:s$
Ramp function	t/T	$[1] \overset{*}{*} \tau[1, -1]^2$	$1:s\tau^2$
		$= \frac{1}{\tau}[1, 2, 3, \ldots]$	

tives higher than the first order. For this reason, it is usually appropriate to treat differential equations in integral form.

As given by Eq. (2.17) the approximative derivative is given by multiplication of the intermediate sequence $S_v(F)$ by the sequence $[1, -1]$. As a first approach, we can take the sequence $S(F)$ instead of $S_v(F)$ and obtain

$$S\left(\frac{dF}{dt}\right) = S(F) * \frac{1}{\tau} [1, -1] - [f_0]$$

In operational calculus, differentiation is obtained by multiplication of the Laplace transform $F(s)$ with the operator s, minus the initial value

$$\mathscr{L}\left[\frac{dF}{dt}\right] = sf(s) - f_0$$

Note the analogy between these two relationships, where the sequence $(1/\tau)[1, -1]$ corresponds to the operator s.

The operations of convolution and deconvolution correspond to the product and the quotient of the corresponding Laplace transform and to the "product" and the "quotient" of the corresponding sequence.

Table 2.14 presents the formal analogy, which can be recognized between some of the operations of impulse analysis and the Laplace transform calculus.

It is possible to make use of this analogy to compute the inverse Laplace transform in some cases where it is difficult to evaluate the integral for the inverse transform: s^{-k} corresponds to

$$\frac{1}{\tau^k} [1, -1]^{-k} = \frac{1}{\tau^k} \left[1, k, \frac{k(k+1)}{2}, \frac{k(k+1)(k+2)}{3!}, \cdots, \right.$$

$$\left. \frac{k(k+1)(k+2)\cdots(k+n-2)}{(n-1)!}\cdots\right]$$

If $k = -1/2$, we obtain

$$f(s) = s^{-\frac{1}{2}} \rightarrow f(t) = \frac{1}{\sqrt{\pi t}}$$

With $\tau = 1$ we obtain

$$[1, -1]^{-\frac{1}{2}} = \left[1, \frac{1}{2}, \frac{1}{2}\frac{1}{2}\left(\frac{1}{2} + 1\right), \frac{1}{2}\frac{1}{3!}\left(\frac{1}{2} + 1\right)\left(\frac{1}{2} + 2\right), \cdots\right]$$

$$= [1, 0.5, 0.375, 0.314, 0.274, 0.247, \ldots]$$

which is a good approximation of sequence corresponding to $S(1/\sqrt{\pi t})$.

It is known that the product of $s^k f(s)$ corresponds to the integral

$$s^k f(s) \rightarrow \frac{1}{\tau^k} \int_0^t u^{k-1} F(t - u) \, du$$

It is not possible to perform this integral for every value of k; the corresponding expression in impulse form is

$$S(s^k f(s)) = \tau^k [1, \, -1]^k * S(F)$$

which allows approximate evaluation of the integral.

CHAPTER 3 Approximate Solution of Differential Equations

INTRODUCTION

The operation with impulse analysis, given in Chapter 2, can be used to obtain an approximation of the solution of differential equations. This chapter considers linear, time-varying, nonlinear and partial differential equations, and describes how to make use of the discrete time approach to solve these equations.

3.1 LINEAR DIFFERENTIAL EQUATIONS

The techniques of integration discussed in Sec. 2.4 may be applied to the integration of differential equations. Consider the linear differential equation

$$a \frac{dx(t)}{dt} + bx(t) = f(t), \qquad x(0) = x_0$$

Integrating this equation from 0 to t yields the integral equation

$$ax(t) - ax_0 + b \int_0^t x(t)\, dt = \int_0^t f(t)\, dt$$

By performing the integration using the trapezoidal rule, in sequence notation we have

$$aS(X) - ax_0[1, 1, 1, \ldots] + b\tau S(X) * [0.5, 1, 1, \ldots] - \frac{b\tau x_0}{2}[1, 1, 1, \ldots]$$

$$= \tau S(F) * [0.5, 1, 1, \ldots] - \frac{\tau f_0}{2}[1, 1, \ldots]$$

$$S(X) * ([a] + b\tau[0.5, 1, 1, \ldots])$$

$$= \left(\left(a + \frac{b\tau}{2}\right)x_0 - \frac{\tau f_0}{2}\right)[1, 1, 1, \ldots] + \tau S(F) * [0.5, 1, 1, \ldots]$$

Thus

$$S(X) = \frac{\tau S(F) * [0.5, 1, 1, 1, \ldots] + ((a + (b\tau/2))x_0 - (\tau f_0/2))[1, 1, 1, \ldots]}{[a] + b\tau[0.5, 1, 1, \ldots]}$$

(3.1)

EXAMPLE 3.1

$$8\frac{dx}{dt} + x = u(t), \qquad x_0 = 0$$

Choose $\tau = 1$:

$$S(X) = \frac{S(F) * [0.5, 1, 1, \ldots] - 0.5[1, 1, 1, \ldots]}{[8] + [0.5, 1, 1, 1, \ldots]}$$

$$= \frac{[0, 1, 2, 3, 4, \ldots]}{[8.5, 1, 1, 1, 1, \ldots]}$$

$$= [0, 0.118, 0.221, 0.313, 0.393, 0.463, 0.527, \ldots]$$

Comparing this with the exact solution $x(t) = (1 - e^{-(t/9)})u(t)$, we have

$$S(X) = [0, 0.119, 0.221, 0.313, 0.393, 0.463, 0.527, \ldots]$$

Evaluation of $S(X)$ by the Madwed-Truxal [23, 42] substitution yields

$$8\frac{dx}{dt} + x(t) = u(t), \qquad x_0 = 0$$

$$X(s) = \frac{1}{S(8s + 1)} = \frac{1/s^2}{8 + (1/s)}$$

$$X(z) = \frac{(\tau^2/6)((z^2 + 4z + 1)/(z - 1)^2)}{8 + (\tau/2)((z + 1)/(z - 1))}$$

For $\tau = 1$,

$$X(z) = \frac{1}{51}\frac{(1 + 4z^{-1} + z^{-2})}{(1 - \frac{32}{17}z^{-1} + \frac{15}{17}z^{-2})}$$

or

$$S(X) = \frac{1}{51} \frac{[1, 4, 1]}{[1, -1.882, 0.882]}$$
$$= [0.019, 0.115, 0.219, 0.311, 0.392, 0.463, 0.526, \ldots]$$

As discussed in Secs. 2.2.3 and 2.2.4, this method yields inaccuracies in the first few terms because it assumes a linear interpolation that is not a good approximation when the function being integrated is discontinuous.

Taking into consideration the discontinuity of $f(t)$, we may integrate $f(t)$ by rectangular integration and $x(t)$ by the trapezoidal rule. Doing this, we have (see Sec. 2.4)

$$8X(z) + \frac{\tau}{2}\left(\frac{z+1}{z-1}\right)X(z) = \left(\frac{\tau}{z-1}\right)F(z) = \frac{\tau^2 z}{(z-1)^2}$$

$$X(z) = \frac{\tau^2 z/(z-1)^2}{8 + (\tau/2)((z+1)/(z-1))}$$

For $\tau = 1$,

$$X(z) = \frac{2z}{17z^2 - 32z + 15}$$

or

$$S(X) = \frac{1}{17} \frac{[0, 2]}{[1, -1.882, 0.882]}$$
$$= [0, 0.118, 0.221, 0.313, 0.394, 0.465, 0.528, \ldots]$$

which compares favorably with the exact solution.

Differential equations may also be integrated by the integration matrix. Using the matrix notation presented in Sec. 2.4, for the differential equation given above we have

$$S(X) = [S(F)\mathbf{B} + ax_0[1, 1, 1, \ldots]]\mathbf{C}^{-1} \tag{3.2}$$

where $\mathbf{C}$ is the matrix†

$$\mathbf{C} = [[\diagdown^a] + b\mathbf{B}]$$

---

† $[\diagdown^a]$ is the diagonal matrix

$$[\diagdown^a] = \begin{bmatrix} a & 0 & 0 & \cdots \\ 0 & a & 0 & \cdots \\ 0 & 0 & a & \cdots \\ \vdots & \vdots & & \ddots \end{bmatrix}$$

For constant a, all diagonal terms are the same and equal to a.

Applying the matrix integration to higher-order differential equations may be accomplished in a similar fashion. For example, the differential equation

$$a\frac{dx^2}{dt^2} + b\frac{dx}{dt} + cx = f(t)$$

is, in sequence notation,

$$S(X) = \{S(F)\mathbf{B}^2 + \tau(a\dot{x}_0 + bx_0)[0, 1, 2, 3, \ldots + ax_0[1, 1, 1, \ldots]\}\mathbf{C}^{-1}$$

where

$$\mathbf{C} = [[\diagdown^a] + b\mathbf{B} + c\mathbf{B}^2]$$

Since the matrix $\mathbf{C}$ is not a function of $S(F)$, it may be evaluated once and used for all forcing functions $S(F)$.

EXAMPLE 3.2

Consider the differential equation

$$\frac{d^2y(x)}{dx^2} = -\frac{w(x)}{K}$$

Integrating this equation twice yields

$$y(x) = -\int_0^x \int_0^v \frac{w(u)}{K}\, du\, dv + C_1 x + C_2$$

where

$$y(0) = 0 = C_2$$

and

$$y(l) = 0 = -\frac{1}{K}\int_0^l \int_0^x w(u)\, du\, dx + C_1 l$$

or

$$C_1 = \frac{1}{lK}\int_0^l \int_0^x w(u)\, du\, dx$$

Thus

$$y(x) = \frac{x}{lK}\int_0^l \int_0^x w(u)\, du\, dx - \frac{1}{K}\int_0^x \int_0^v w(u)\, du\, dv$$

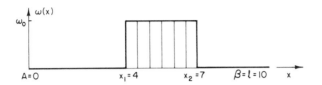

FIG. 3.1 Example 3.2.

These integrations may be performed by any of the methods presented in Sec. 2.4.

Consider the case where $w(x)$ is as depicted in Fig. 3.1. For this case, with $\tau = 1$, we have

$$S(W) = \omega_0[0, 0, 0, 0, 1, 1, 1, 0, 0, 0]$$

The second integral is $S(\omega)$ is

$$S(W) * [0, 1, 2, 3, \ldots] = \omega_0[0, 0, 0, 0, 0, 1, 3, 6, 10, 14, 18]$$

Thus

$$C_1 = \frac{\omega_0}{lK}(18) = 1.8\frac{\omega_0}{K}$$

$$S(C_1x) = \frac{\omega_0}{K}1.8[0, 1, 2, 3, 4, 5, 6, 7, 8, 9, 10]$$

$$= \frac{\omega_0}{K}[0, 1.8, 3.6, 5.4, 7.2, 9.0, 10.8, 12.6, 14.4, 16.2, 18]$$

and

$$S(Y) = S(C_1x) - \frac{1}{K}S(W) * [0, 1, 2, 3, \ldots]$$

$$= \frac{\omega_0}{K}[0, 1.8, 3.6, 5.4, 7.2, 8.0, 7.8, 6.6, 4.4, 2.2, 0]$$

For this distribution the analytical solution may be determined for $0 < x < x_1$ as

$$y(x) = \frac{\omega_0}{K}\left[\frac{x}{l}\left\{(l - x_2)(x_2 - x_1) + \frac{(x_2 - x_1)^2}{2}\right\}\right]$$

For $x_1 < x < x_2$,

$$y(x) = \frac{\omega_0}{K}\left[\frac{x}{l}\left\{(l - x_2)(x_2 - x_1) + \frac{(x_2 - x_1)^2}{2}\right\} - \frac{(x - x_1)^2}{2}\right]$$

For $x_1 < x < l$,

$$y(x) = \frac{\omega_0}{K} \left[\frac{x}{l} \left\{ (l - x_2)(x_2 - x_1) + \frac{(x_2 - x_1)^2}{2} \right\} \right.$$

$$\left. \frac{(x_2 - x_1)^2}{2} - (x_2 - x_1)(x - x_2) \right]$$

For $l = 10$, $x_1 = 4$, and $x_2 = 7$, we have the exact sequence

$$S(Y) = \frac{\omega_0}{K} [0, 1.35, 2.7, 4.05, 5.4, 6.25, 6.1, 4.95, 3.3, 1.65, 0]$$

Greater accuracy may be obtained if $\omega(x)$ is approximated by the sequence (see Problem 3.5 in Appendix):

$$S_2(\omega) = \omega_0[0, 0, 0, 0, 0.5, 1, 1, 0.5, 0, 0, 0]$$

For this sequence (call it $S_2(\omega)$) we have $C_1 = 1.35(\omega_0/K)$ and

$$S(Y) = S(C_1 x) - \frac{1}{K} S_2(\omega) * [0, 1, 2, 3, 4, \ldots]$$

$$= [0, 1.35, 2.7, 4.05, 5.4, 6.25, 6.1, 4.95, 3.3, 1.65, 0]$$

Of course any distribution $\omega(x)$ may be integrated by this method.

EXAMPLE 3.3

Consider the differential equation

$$\frac{d^4 y}{dx^4} = \omega(x)$$

The boundary conditions are

$$y(0) = y'(0) = y(l) = y'(l) = 0$$

Thus

$$y(x) = \int \int_0^x \int \int \omega(x)(dx)^4 + y''(0) \frac{x^2}{2} + y'''(0) \frac{x^3}{3!}$$

The terms $y''(0)$ and $y'''(0)$ must be determined from the boundary conditions $y(l) = y'(l) = 0$.

Three integrations of the differential equation yield

$$\frac{dy}{dx} = \int \int_0^x \int \omega(x)(dx)^3 + y''(0)x + y'''(0) \frac{x^2}{2}$$

In sequence notation,

$$S(Y) = S(W) * \frac{1}{3!} [0, 1, 2^3, 3^3, 4^3, \ldots]$$

$$+ \frac{y''(0)}{2} [0, 1, 2^2, 3^2, 4^2, \ldots]$$

$$+ \frac{y'''(0)}{3!} [0, 1, 2^3, 3^3, 4^3, \ldots]$$

and

$$S(Y') = S\left(\frac{dy}{dx}\right) = S(W) * \frac{1}{2} [0, 1, 2^2, 3^2, 4^2, \ldots]$$

$$+ y''(0)[0, 1, 2, 3, 4, \ldots] + \frac{y'''(0)}{2} [0, 1, 2^2, 3^2, 4^2, \ldots]$$

Evaluation of these sequences yields values for $y(l)$ and $y'(l)$ in terms of and $y'''(0)$. These relations determine the values of $y''(0)$ and $y'''(0)$. In particular consider the case where $\omega(x)$ is a concentrated load of magnitude W acting at x_1 as shown in Fig. 3.2.

FIG. **3.2** Example 3.3.

For $x_1 = 3$, $l = 6$, and $\tau = 1$, we have

$$S(W) = W[0, 0, 0, 1, 0, 0, 0]$$

$$S(Y) = \frac{W}{6} [0, 0, 0, 0, 1, 8, 27]$$

$$+ \frac{y''(0)}{2} [0, 1, 4, 9, 16, 25, 36]$$

$$+ \frac{y'''(0)}{6} [0, 1, 8, 27, 64, 125, 216]$$

and

$$S(Y') = \frac{W}{2} [0, 0, 0, 0, 1, 4, 9]$$

$$+ y'(0)[0, 1, 2, 3, 4, 5, 6]$$

$$+ \frac{y''(0)}{2} [0, 1, 4, 9, 16, 25, 36]$$

Evaluating the last term of the sequences to determine $y''(0)$ and $y'''(0)$,

$$0 = y(l) = y_6 = \frac{27W}{6} + y''(0)\frac{36}{2} + y'''(0)\frac{216}{6}$$

$$0 = y'(l) = y'_6 = \frac{9W}{2} + y''(0)6 + y'''(0)\frac{36}{2}$$

Solving for $y''(0)$ and $y'''(0)$,

$$y''(0) = \tfrac{3}{4}W \qquad \text{and} \qquad y'''(0) = -\tfrac{1}{2}W$$

Thus

$$S(Y) = W\{\tfrac{1}{6}[0, 0, 0, 0, 1, 9, 27] + \tfrac{3}{8}[0, 1, 4, 9, 16, 25, 36]$$
$$- \tfrac{1}{12}[0, 1, 8, 27, 64, 125, 216]\}$$
$$= [0, 0.29166, 0.83333, 1.125, 0.83333, 0.29166, 0]$$

For this distribution the analytical solution is known. For $l = 3$ and $0 < x < l/2$:

$$y(x) = W\left[\frac{x^3}{12} - \frac{lx^2}{16}\right]$$

for $l/2 < x < l$

$$y(x) = W\left[\frac{x^3}{12} - \frac{3x^2}{8}\right]$$

and the exact sequence

$$S(Y) = W[0, 0.29166, 0.83333, 1.125, 0.83333, 0.29166, 0]$$

Differential equations containing a time delay may be solved in a similar fashion, using the delay operator. Consider the equation

$$a\frac{dx}{dt} + bx(t - \tau_i) = f(t)$$

$$a(x(t) - x_0) + b\int_0^t x(t - \tau_i)\, dt = \int_0^t f(t)\, dt$$

Choosing τ sufficiently small for the desired accuracy and such that $\theta = \tau_i/\tau$ is an integer, we have

$$aS(x) - ax_0[1, 1, 1, \ldots] + \tau b([S(x)D(-\theta)] * [0.5, 1, 1, \ldots])$$

$$= \tau S(F) * [0.5, 1, 1, 1, \ldots] - \frac{\tau f_0}{2} [1, 1, 1, \ldots]$$

EXAMPLE 3.4

For the equation

$$8 \frac{dx}{dt} + x(t - 4) = u(t), \qquad x_0 = 0$$

and $\tau = 1$, we have

$$S(X) = \frac{[1, 2, 3, \ldots]}{[8, 0, 0, 0, 0.5, 1, 1, 1, \ldots]}$$

$$= [0.1250, 0.2500, 0.3750, 0.5000, 0.546875, 0.525391,$$
$$0.584717, 0.636627, 0.682049, 0.721793, \ldots]$$

3.2 TIME-VARYING DIFFERENTIAL EQUATIONS

To solve differential equations with time-varying coefficients we need know only the sequence of the coefficients and the sequence representation of the following operations, which are easily verified †:

$$\int_0^t a(u)x(u)\, du = S(X)[\diagdown^a]\mathbf{B}$$

$$\int_0^t a(u)\dot{x}(u)\, du = a(u)X(u)\Big|_0^t - \int_0^t \dot{a}(u)x(u)\, du$$

$$= S(X)[\diagdown^a] - a_0x_0[1, 1, 1, \ldots] - S(X)[\diagdown^{\dot{a}}]\mathbf{B}$$

$$\int_0^t \int_0^v a(u)x(u)\, du\, dv = S(X)[\diagdown^a]\mathbf{B}^2$$

$$\int_0^t \int_0^v a(u)\dot{x}(u)\, du\, dv = S(X)[\diagdown^a]\mathbf{B} - a_0x_0[1, 1, 1, \ldots] - S(X)[\diagdown^{\dot{a}}]\mathbf{B}^2$$

---

† For $a = a(t)$ and $S(A) = [a_0, a_1, a_2, \ldots]$,

$$[\diagdown^a] = \begin{bmatrix} a_0 & 0 & 0 & \cdots \\ 0 & a_1 & 0 & \cdots \\ 0 & 0 & a_2 & \\ \vdots & \vdots & & \ddots \end{bmatrix}$$

Consider the equation

$$a(t)\frac{dx}{dt} + b(t)x = f(t), \qquad x(0) = x_0$$

or

$$\int_0^t a(u)\dot{x}(u)\, du + \int_0^t b(u)x(u)\, du = \int_0^t f(u)\, du$$

In matrix notation we have

$$S(X)[\diagup^a] - S(X)[\diagup^d]\mathbf{B} - ax_0[1, 1, 1, \ldots] + S(X)[\diagup^b]\mathbf{B} = S(F)\mathbf{B}$$

Thus

$$S(X) = (S(F)\mathbf{B} + a_0x_0[1, 1, \ldots, 1, \ldots])\mathbf{C}^{-1} \tag{3.3}$$

where

$$\mathbf{C} = [\diagup^a] + [\diagup^{b-d}]\mathbf{B}$$

EXAMPLE 3.5

Consider the Legendre equation:

$$\frac{d^2x}{dt^2} - \frac{2t}{1 - t^2}\frac{dx}{dt} + \frac{6}{1 - t^2}x = 0$$

$$x(0) = -0.5, \qquad \dot{x}(0) = 0$$

with $(\tau = 0.1)$.† We have the solution shown in Fig. 3.3. For small

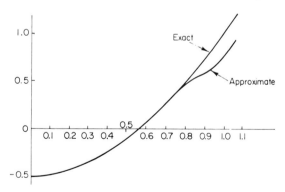

FIG. 3.3   Solution of the Legendre equation.

---

† This example for $(\tau = 0.1)$ is worked by Ronveaux [35].

$x(0 \leq x \leq 0.75)$, the accuracy is good. In the vicinity of $t = 1$ ($b(t) \to \infty$), the solution diverges, as would be expected.

Equations with time-varying coefficients may also be solved in sequence notation to yield a tabular algorithm for the solution sequence.

Consider the equation

$$\frac{dy}{dt} + a(t)y(t) = f(t), \qquad y(0) = y_0$$

or

$$y(t) + \int_0^t a(x)y(x)\,dx = \int_0^t f(x)\,dx + y_0 = C(t)$$

Evaluation of the integrals by trapezoidal rule for the values $t = n\tau$ ($n = 0, 1, 2, \ldots$) yields

$$y_0 = y(0), \qquad y_1 + \tau\left(\frac{a_0 y_0}{2} + \frac{a_1 y_1}{2}\right) = C_1$$

or

$$y_1 = \frac{C_1 - (\tau a_0 y_0/2)}{1 + (\tau a_1/2)} = \frac{C_1 - \Sigma_1}{\alpha_1}$$

$$y_2 + \tau\left(\frac{a_0 y_0}{2} + a_1 y_1 + \frac{a_2 y_2}{2}\right) = C_2$$

or

$$y_2 = \frac{C_2 - \tau((a_0 y_0/2) + a_1 y_1)}{1 + \tau(a_2/2)} = \frac{C_2 - \Sigma_2}{\alpha_2}$$

In general

$$y_n = \frac{C_n - \Sigma_n}{\alpha_n} \tag{3.4}$$

where

$$\Sigma_n = \tau\left(\frac{a_0 y_0}{2} + a_1 y_1 + a_2 y_2 + \cdots + a_{n-1} y_{n-1}\right)$$

and

$$\alpha_n = 1 + \frac{\tau a_n}{2}$$

This operation may be tabulated by the following algorithm (for $n \geq 1$):

n	a_n	$\alpha_n = 1 + \dfrac{\tau}{2}a_n$	C_n	$y_n = \dfrac{C_n - \Sigma_n}{\alpha_n}$	$\dfrac{\tau}{2}a_0$	τa_1	τa_2	τa_3	$\cdots$
0	a_0	$\times\times\times$	y_0	$\times\times\times$	$\dfrac{\tau a_0 y_0}{2}$	$\dfrac{\tau a_0 y_0}{2}$	$\dfrac{\tau a_0 y_0}{2}$	$\dfrac{\tau a_0 y_0}{2}$	$\cdots$
1	a_1	$1 + \dfrac{\tau a_1}{2} = \alpha_1$	C_1	$y_1 = \dfrac{C_1 - \Sigma_1}{\alpha_1}$	Σ_1	$\tau a_1 y_1$	$\tau a_1 y_1$	$\tau a_1 y_1$	$\cdots$
2	a_2	$1 + \dfrac{\tau a_2}{2} = \alpha_2$	C_2	$y_2 = \dfrac{C_2 - \Sigma_2}{\alpha_2}$		Σ_2	$\tau a_2 y_2$	$\tau a_2 y_2$	$\cdots$
3	a_3	$1 + \dfrac{\tau a_3}{2} = \alpha_3$	C_3	$y_3 = \dfrac{C_3 - \Sigma_3}{\alpha_3}$			Σ_3	$\tau a_3 y_3$	$\cdots$
4	a_4	$1 + \dfrac{\tau a_4}{2} = \alpha_4$	C_4					Σ_4	
5	a_5	$1 + \dfrac{\tau a_5}{2} = \alpha_5$	C_5						

EXAMPLE 3.6

Consider the equation

$$\frac{dy}{dt} + ty(t) = tu(t), \qquad y(0) = 0$$

with $y_0 = 0$ and $\tau = 0.4$;

$$C(t) = \frac{t^2}{2} u(t)$$

n	a_n	$\alpha_n = 1 + \dfrac{\tau}{2}a_n$	C_n	$y_n = \dfrac{C_n - \Sigma_n}{\alpha_n}$	$\dfrac{\tau a_0}{2} = 0$	$\tau a_1 = 0.16$	$\tau a_2 = 0.32$	$\tau a_3 = 0.48$
0	0	$\times\times\times$	0	$\times\times\times$	0	0	0	0
1	0.4	1.08	0.08	0.074	$\Sigma_1 = 0$	0.0119	0.0119	0.0119
2	0.8	1.16	0.32	0.266		0.0119	0.0851	0.0851
3	1.2	1.24	0.72	0.502			0.0970	0.241
4	1.6	1.32	1.28	0.714				0.338
5	2.0	1.40	2.0					
⋮	⋮							

$$S(Y) = [0, 0.074, 0.266, 0.502, 0.714, \ldots]$$

For the second-order differential equation,

$$\frac{d^2y}{dt^2} + a(t)\frac{dy}{dt} + b(t)y(t) = f(t)$$

$$y(0) = y_0, \qquad \dot{y}(0) = \dot{y}_0$$

or

$$[1 + a(t)]y(t) - \int_0^t \dot{a}(t)y(t)\,dt + \int_0^t\!\!\int b(t)y(t)(dt)^2$$

$$= (1 + a_0)y_0 + \dot{y}_0 t + \int_0^t\!\!\int f(t)(dt)^2 = C(t)$$

Define

$$1 + a(t) = u(t) \qquad \text{and} \qquad \dot{a}(t) = v(t)$$

Then

$$u(t)y(t) - \int_0^t v(t)y(t)\,dt + \int_0^t\!\!\int b(t)y(t)(dt)^2 = C(t)$$

Evaluating by trapezoidal rule we have

$$S\left(\int_0^t\!\!\int b(t)y(t)(dt)^2\right) = \tau^2[S(B)S(Y)] * [0.5, 1, 1, \ldots]^2$$

$$- \frac{\tau^2}{2} b_0 y_0[1, 1, 1, \ldots] * [0.5, 1, 1, 1, \ldots]$$

$$= \tau^2[S(B)S(Y)] * [0.25, 1, 2, 3, \ldots]$$

$$- \frac{\tau^2}{2} b_0 y_0[0.5, 1.5, 2.5, 3.5, \ldots]$$

$$= \tau^2[0.25 b_0 y_0, \ 0.25 b_0 y_0 + b_1 y_1, \ 0.25 b_0 y_0 + b_1 y_1 + 2b_2 y_2, \ldots]$$

$$- \tau^2 \frac{b_0 y_0}{2}[0.5, 1.5, 2.5, 3.5, \ldots]$$

Evaluating term by term we have

$$y_0 = y(0)$$

$$u_1 y_1 - \tau\left(\frac{v_0 y_0}{2} + \frac{v_1 y_1}{2}\right) + \tau^2(0.25 b_0 y_0 + b_1 y_1) - \tau^2 \frac{b_0 y_0}{2}(1.5) = C_1$$

or

$$y_1 = \frac{C_1 + (\tau/2)(v_0 + b_0\tau)y_0}{u_1 - (\tau v_1/2) + \tau^2 b_1} = \frac{C_1 + \Sigma_1}{\alpha_1}$$

$$y_2 = \frac{C_2 + \tau(v_1 - \tau b_1)y_1 + (\tau/2)(v_0 - 2\tau b_0)y_0}{u_2 - (\tau v_2/2) + 2\tau^2 b_2} = \frac{C_2 + \Sigma_2}{\alpha_2}$$

In general, for the nth term,

$$y_n = \frac{C_n + (\tau \sum_{k=1}^{n-1} (v_k - k\tau b_k)y_k) + (\tau/2)(v_0 - n\tau b_0)y_0}{u_n - (\tau v_n/2) + n\tau^2 b_n}$$

$$= \frac{C_n + \Sigma_n}{\alpha_n} \tag{3.5}$$

which may be evaluated by a tabular algorithm similar to that used above for the first-order differential equation. The tabular algorithms or the equation for the general term are easily adapted to use on a digital computer.

This technique may, of course, be applied to a higher-order equation. When the coefficient functions and initial conditions are given, the expressions are frequently simplified.

3.3 NONLINEAR DIFFERENTIAL EQUATIONS

Nonlinear differential equations of the form

$$a(x)\frac{dx}{dt} + b(x)x(t) = f(t)$$

may be solved by approximating $a(x)$ and $b(x)$ by piecewise constant functions of x. For example, let

$$a(x) \doteq a(x_n) = a_n \quad \text{and} \quad b(x) \doteq b(x_n) = b_n \quad \text{for} \quad x_n \le x < x_v$$

Within each interval the linear equation is solved. This reduces the solution of the nonlinear equation to the solution of a sequence of linear differential equations, with the final conditions of one forming the initial conditions of the next.

EXAMPLE 3.7

Consider the circuit containing a nonlinear inductance $L(i)$ shown in Fig. 3.4, where

$$e(t) = Eu(t) \quad \text{and} \quad i(0) = 0$$

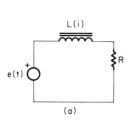 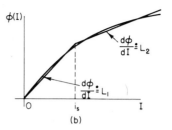

(a) (b)

FIG. 3.4   *RL* circuit containing nonlinear inductor.

The differential equation of the system is

$$Eu(t) = L(i)\frac{di}{dt} + Ri(t)$$

or

$$T(i)\frac{di}{dt} + i(t) = I_0$$

where

$$T(i) = \frac{L(i)}{R} \quad \text{and} \quad I_0 = \frac{E}{R}$$

For $(0 \le i \le i_s)$,

$$T(i) \doteq \frac{L_1}{R} = T_1$$

and for $(i \ge i_s)$

$$T(i) \doteq \frac{L_2}{R} = T_2$$

In the first region, $(i < i_s)$,

$$T_1\frac{di}{dt} + i(t) = I_0, \qquad i(0) = 0$$

and from Sec. 3.1,

$$\frac{S(I)}{I_0} = \frac{\tau[1, 1, 1, \ldots] * [0.5, 1, 1, \ldots] - 0.5\tau[1, 1, 1, \ldots]}{[T_1 + 0.5, 1, 1, 1, \ldots]}$$

$$= \frac{\tau[0, 1, 2, 3, \ldots]}{[T_1 + 0.5, 1, 1, 1, \ldots]}$$

which is the sequence for $i(t)$ for $i(t) < i_s$. For $i(t) > i_s$ we have (taking $t = 0$ as the point where $i(t) = i_s$)

$$T_2 \frac{di}{dt} + i(t) = T_0, \qquad i(0) = i_s$$

so

$$\frac{S(I)}{I_0} = \frac{\tau[1, 1, 1, \ldots] * [0.5, 1, 1, 1, \ldots] + [(T_2 + (\tau/2))i_s - (\tau/2)][1, 1, 1, \ldots]}{[T_2 + 0.5, 1, 1, 1, \ldots]}$$

Suppose $I_0 = 1$, $i_s = 0.4$, $T_1 = 8$, $T_2 = 3$, and $i_0 = 0$. Taking $\tau = 1$, for $i(t) < 0.4$ we have

$$S_1(I) = \frac{[1, 1, 1, \ldots] * [0.5, 1, 1, 1, \ldots] - 0.5[1, 1, 1, \ldots]}{[8.5, 1, 1, 1, \ldots]}$$

$$= \frac{[0, 1, 2, 3, \ldots]}{[8.5, 1, 1, 1, \ldots]} = [0, 0.118, 0.221, 0.313, 0.394, 0.465]$$

Since the term $i_5 > 0.4 = i_s$, we use the expression with $T_1 = T_2$ for $S(I)$ in the region $i(t) > 0.4$:

$$S_2(I) = \frac{[1, 1, 1, \ldots] * [0.5, 1, 1, 1, \ldots] + ((3.5)(0.4) - 0.5)[1, 1, 1, \ldots]}{[3.5, 1, 1, 1, \ldots]}$$

$$= \frac{[1.4, 2.4, 3.4, 4.4, \ldots]}{[3.5, 1, 1, 1, \ldots]}$$

$$= [0.400, 0.571, 0.694, 0.781, 0.844, 0.888, 0.920, 0.943,$$
$$0.959, 0.971, 0.979, 0.985, 0.989, 0.992, 0.995, \ldots]$$

Figure 3.5 is a sketch of $i(t)$.

Usually the nonlinearity may not be assumed piecewise constant and must be taken into consideration at each stage of the computation. Thus the nonlinear differential equation must be solved for the general nonlinearity.

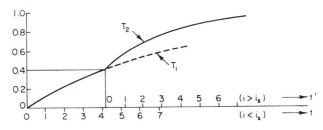

FIG. **3.5** Example 3.7.

Consider the equation

$$\frac{dy}{dt} + a(y)y(t) = f(t), \qquad y(0) = y_0$$

or

$$y(t) + \int_0^t a(y)y(t)\, dt = \int_0^t f(t)\, dt + y_0 = C(t)$$

Performing the integration by trapezoidal rule yields for the second term (y_1) of $S(Y)$:

$$y_1 + \frac{\tau y_0 a(y_0)}{2} + \frac{\tau y_1 a(y_1)}{2} = C_1$$

or

$$\frac{y_1}{C_1 - (\tau/2)y_0 a(y_0)} = \frac{y_1}{C_1 - \tau \sum_1} = \frac{y_1}{B_1} = \frac{1}{1 + (\tau/2)a(y_1)}$$

Determination of y_1 depends upon the solution of this nonlinear algebraic equation. This equation may be solved graphically, as in Fig. 3.6.

Of course graphical solutions are not well suited for digital computer applications. However, the above algebraic equation may be solved by any iteration scheme. For example, a first approximation of y_1 is

$$y_1^{(1)} = B_1 \frac{1}{1 + (\tau/2)a(y_1)} \approx B_1$$

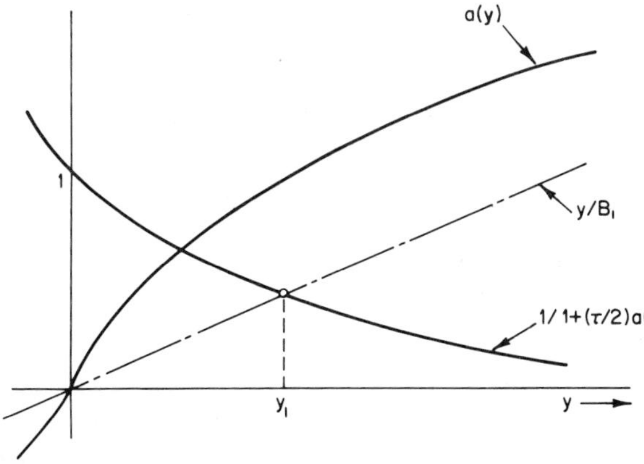

FIG. **3.6** Graphical solution of the nonlinear algebraic equation.

and the iteration may proceed:

$$y_1^{(n)} = B_1 \frac{1}{1 + (\tau/2)a(y_1^{(n-1)})}$$

or the equation

$$\frac{y_1}{B_1} - \frac{1}{1 + (\tau/2)a(y_1)} = 0$$

may be solved by a root-seeking program such as the Newton-Raphson method. Likewise, to find y_2, we take

$$y_2 + \frac{\tau}{2} y_0 a(y_0) + \tau y_1 a(y_1) + \frac{\tau}{2} y_2 a(y_2) = C_2$$

or

$$\frac{y_2}{C_2 - ((\tau/2)y_0 a(y_0) + \tau y_1 a(y_1))} = \frac{y_2}{C_2 - \tau \sum_2} = \frac{y_2}{B_2} = \frac{1}{1 + (\tau/2)a(y_2)}$$

Note that the expression on the right is the same as that obtained for y_1. Thus we must solve the same algebraic equation, with possibly a different value for B_2. In general

$$\frac{y_n}{C_n - (\tau \sum_{k=1}^{n-1} y_k a(y_k)) - (\tau/2)y_0 a(y_0)} = \frac{y_n}{C - \tau \sum_n}$$

$$= \frac{y_n}{B_n} = \frac{1}{1 + (\tau/2)a(y_n)}$$

and the equation

$$B_l = y_l\left(1 + \frac{\tau}{2} a(y_l)\right) \tag{3.6}$$

may be solved in the range of y that is of interest, with sufficiently small increments (an easy task) of y_l to yield an accurate relationship $B_l(y_l)$ or $y_l(B_l)$ through interpolation.† The procedure then becomes one of evaluating B_n and looking up (possibly with interpolation) the associated value of y_n. Thus, along with the function $a(y)$, we must store in the computer the function

$$B(y) = y\left(1 + \frac{\tau}{2} a(y)\right)$$

---

† It is assumed here that B is a single-valued function of y. If this is not the case, (due to the nature of $a(y)$), then special care must be taken in the representation of $B(y)$.

The computation of B_n follows the algorithm shown in the accompanying tabulation.

n	y_n	$a(y_n)$	$B_n = C_n - \tau \sum_n$	C_n			
0	y_0	$a(y_0)$		C_0	$\frac{1}{2}y_0a(y_0)$	$\frac{1}{2}y_0a(y_0)$	$\frac{1}{2}y_0a(y_0)$
1	y_1	$a(y_1)$	$B_1 = C_1 - \tau \sum_1$	C_1	$\sum_1$	$y_1a(y_1)$	$y_1a(y_1)$
2	y_2	$a(y_2)$	$B_2 = C_2 - \tau \sum_2$	C_2		$\sum_2$	$y_2a(y_2)$
3			$B_3 = C_3 - \tau \sum_3$	C_3			$\sum_3$
4				C_4			
5				C_5			

The calculation may be somewhat simplified by observing that

$$B_n = C_n - C_{n-1} + B_{n-1} - \tau y_{n-1}a(y_{n-1})$$

which requires beginning with the calculation of B_1 and y_1:

$$B_2 = C_2 - C_1 + B_1 - \tau y_1 a(y_1)$$

EXAMPLE 3.8

Consider the equation with known exact solution

$$\frac{dy}{dt} + y^2 = 1, \qquad y(0) = 0$$

In the notation

$$\frac{dy}{dt} + a(y)y(t) = f(t)$$

we have

$$a(y) = y, \qquad f(t) = 1 \qquad \text{and} \qquad y_0 = 0$$

Thus $C(t) = tu(t)$.

In this case $y(B)$ may be expressed explicitly, since

$$B = y\left(1 + \frac{T}{2}y\right)$$

or

$$\frac{T}{2}y^2 + y - B = 0, \qquad y = \frac{1}{\tau}(\sqrt{1 + 2TB} - 1)$$

For $\tau = 0.2$,

$$y = 5(\sqrt{1 + 0.4B} - 1), \qquad \text{and} \qquad S(C) = [0, 0.2, 0.4, 0.6, 0.8, \ldots]$$

$$B_1 = C_1 - \tau \Sigma_1 = C_1 - \frac{\tau}{2} y_0 a(y_0) = C_1 = 0.2$$

$$y_1 = 5(\sqrt{1.08} - 1) = \underline{0.19615}$$

$$B_2 = C_2 - C_1 + B_1 - \tau y_1 a(y_1)$$
$$= 0.4 - 0.2 + 0.2 - 0.2(0.19615)^2 = 0.407695$$

$$y_2 = 5(\sqrt{1.163078} - 1) = \underline{0.3923}$$

Continuing the process, we obtain the sequence

$$S(Y) = [0, 0.19615, 0.39230, 0.546995, 0.671925, 0.76782, 0.838545, \ldots]$$

Comparing with the exact sequence $(y(t) = \tanh(t))$,

$$S(Y) = [0, 0.19738, 0.37995, 0.53705, 0.66404, 0.76159, 0.83365, \ldots]$$

We find that even with a sample interval of $\tau = 0.2$, the error is less than 1 percent.

This technique may, of course, be applied to higher-order nonlinear differential equations.

Nonlinear differential equations may also be solved by the discrete differential approximations of Sec. 2.5. For the preceding example, using the *back difference*,

$$\frac{dy}{dt} + y^2 = 1, \qquad y(0) = y_0 = 0$$

$$\frac{1}{\tau} S(Y) * [1, -1] + S(Y)S(Y) = [1, 1, 1, 1, \ldots]$$

Thus

$$y_n - y_{n-1} + \tau y_n^2 = \tau$$

or

$$y_n = \sqrt{(1/4\tau^2) + 1 + (1/\tau)y_{n-1}} - \frac{1}{2\tau}$$

which yields (for $\tau = 0.2$)

$$S(Y) = [0, 0.192582, 0.404109, 0.544757, 0.697465, 0.814713, 0.901995, \ldots]$$

Using the *forward difference* (see Sec. 2.5),

$$y_{n+1} - y_n + \tau y_n^2 = \tau \qquad \text{or} \qquad y_{n+1} = y_n - \tau y_n^2 + \tau$$

which yields (for $\tau = 0.2$)

$$S(Y) = [0, 0.20, 0.392, 0.561267, 0.698263, 0.800749, 0.872509, \ldots]$$

The estimate $(1/\tau)(y_n - y_{n-1})$ best approximates the derivative at the intermediate value (*central difference*). Thus a more accurate result is obtained with

$$\frac{1}{\tau}(y_n - y_{n-1}) + (y_{n-1}^v)^2 = 1$$

and

$$(y_{n-1}^v)^2 = \left(\frac{y_{n-1} + y_n}{2}\right)^2 = \frac{1}{4}(y_n^2 + 2y_n y_{n-1} + y_{n-1}^2) \approx y_n y_{n-1}$$

With this estimate for y^2, we have (for $\tau = 0.2$)

$$y_n - y_{n-1} + \tau y_n y_{n-1} = \tau \qquad \text{or} \qquad y_n = \frac{y_{n-1} + \tau}{1 + \tau y_{n-1}}$$

and

$$S(Y) = [0, 0.20, 0.384615, 0.542857, 0.670103, 0.767273, 0.838588, \ldots]$$

Using the estimate

$$(y_{n-1}^v)^2 = \tfrac{1}{4}(y_n^2 + 2y_n y_{n-1} + y_{n-1}^2)$$

yields (for $\tau = 0.2$)

$$y_n = \frac{2}{\tau}\left[\sqrt{1 + \tau^2 + 2\tau y_{n-1}} - \left(1 + \frac{\tau}{2}y_{n-1}\right)\right]$$

and

$$S(Y) = [0, 0.19804, 0.38126, 0.53892, 0.66627, 0.76398, 0.83599, \ldots]$$

The comparative accuracy of the methods exemplified above may be determined by comparing with

$$y_5 \doteq y(1) = 0.76159$$

This comparison is presented in Table 3.1.

TABLE 3.1
EXAMPLE 3.8 ($\tau = 0.2$)

y_5	Percent error	Technique
0.76159	$\cdots$	Exact solution
0.76782	0.8	$B_n = C_n - C_{n-1} + B_{n-1} - \tau y_{n-1} a(y_{n-1})$
0.81471	7.0	Back difference
0.80075	5.1	Forward difference
0.76727	0.7	Central difference $(y_n y_{n-1})$
0.76398	0.3	Central difference $\frac{1}{4}(y_n{}^2 + 2y_n y_{n-1} + y_{n-1}{}^2)$

3.4 PARTIAL DIFFERENTIAL EQUATIONS

Impulse analysis may be applied to the solution of partial differential equations. The application will be demonstrated through several examples. For the details of the numerical solution of partial differential equations, the reader is referred to Cuénod [7] and Richtmyer [33].

EXAMPLE 3.9

Consider the lossless transmission of a pressure wave through a pipe of length l, taking into account the elasticity of the pipe and water. The transmission equations are

$$-\frac{\partial h}{\partial x} = \frac{w}{z}\frac{\partial v}{\partial t}, \qquad -\frac{\partial v}{\partial x} = \frac{1}{wz}\frac{\partial h}{\partial t}$$

where

h = pressure
v = velocity of the water
w = wave velocity
$z = wmH_r/v_r$ = characteristic coefficient of transmission, for which

H_r, v_r = reference values of h and v

The solution of these equations has the form

$$h(x, t) = A\left(t - \frac{x}{w}\right) + B\left(t + \frac{x}{w}\right)$$

$$v(x, t) = \frac{A(t - (x/w))}{z} - \frac{B(t + (x/w))}{z}$$

with the boundary conditions

$$h(0, t) = f(t) - z_1 v_1(0, t) \qquad \text{and} \qquad h(l, t) = z_2 v(l, t)$$

Letting $T = l/w$ and $T_x = x/w$, we have

$$S(H) = S(F) * \frac{[(1 - r_1)/2]D(T_x - T) + [((1 - r_1)r_2)/2]D(T - T_x)}{[1]D(-T) - [r_1 r_2]D(T)}$$

$$= S(F) * \frac{[(1 - r_1)/2]D(T_x) + [((1 - r_1)r_2)/2]D(2T - T_x)}{[1] - [r_1 r_2]D(2T)}$$

where

$$r_1 = \frac{z_1 - z}{z_1 + z} = \text{source reflection coefficient}$$

$$r_2 = \frac{z_2 - z}{z_2 + z} = \text{terminal reflection coefficient}$$

For $T_x = 2$ and $T = 5$, we have

$$S(H) = \frac{1 - r_1}{2} S(F) * \frac{[0, 0, 1, 0, 0, 0, 0, r_2]}{[1, 0, 0, 0, 0, 0, 0, 0, 0, 0, 0, -r_1 r_2]}$$

$$= \frac{1 - r_1}{2} S(F) * [0, 0, 1, 0, 0, 0, 0, 0, -r_2, 0, 0, 0, r_1 r_2, \ldots]$$

Using the notation $[a, 0, 0, 0, 0, b, \ldots] = [a, 4 \times 0, b, \ldots]$

$$S(H) = \frac{1 - r_1}{2} S(F) * [0, 0, 1, 5 \times 0, -r_2, 3 \times 0, r_1 r_2,$$

$$5 \times 0, -r_1 r_2, 3 \times 0, r_1^2, r_2^2, \ldots]$$

Thus, if $f(t)$ is a short rectangular pulse, we have $h(2w, t)$, as shown in Fig. 3.7.

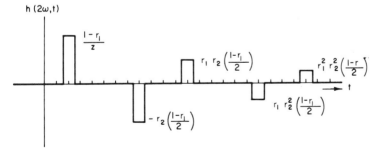

FIG. 3.7   Example 3.9 ($T_x = 2$, $T = 5$).

If $h(0, t) = f(t)$ is an arbitrary function, the total waveform may be constructed by the convolution of the impulse approximations of $f(t)$, with the results given above. This system exhibits a resonance phenomenon that may, of course, be investigated by application of the above methods.

EXAMPLE 3.10

Consider the case of transmission with losses along a long transmission line. This transmission satisfies the equations

$$-\frac{\partial V}{\partial x} = RI + L\frac{\partial I}{\partial t}, \qquad -\frac{\partial I}{\partial x} = GV + C\frac{\partial V}{\partial t}$$

where I is the current, V the voltage, R, L, G, and C the resistance, inductance, conductance, and capacitance per unit length, respectively. If the voltage at the end of the line ($x = 0$) is a step of magnitude E_m, the solution is (see Cuénod [7])

$$V(x, t) = \begin{cases} 0 \quad \text{for } t < \dfrac{x}{w} \\[2ex] e^{-(ax/\omega)} - \displaystyle\int_{ax/\omega}^{at} e^{-\theta}\frac{1}{\sqrt{\theta^2 - (ax/w)}}; \; J_1(j\sqrt{\theta^2 - (ax/w)}) \, d\theta \\[3ex] \hspace{10cm} \text{for } t \geq \dfrac{x}{w} \end{cases}$$

where

$$a = \frac{1}{2}\frac{LG + CR}{LC}$$

$$J_1 = \text{Bessel function of first order}$$

The preceding integral may be evaluated by the techniques outlined in Sec. 2.4. For

$$R = 0.123 \; \Omega/\text{km}, \qquad L = 1.32 \; \text{mh/km}, \qquad C = 0.88 \times 10^{-2} \; \mu\text{F/km}$$

$$G = 0, \qquad a = \frac{R}{2L} = 46.5/\text{s}, \qquad \omega = \frac{1}{\sqrt{LC}} = 2.9 \times 10^5 \; \text{km/s}$$

$$x = 6250 \; \text{km}, \qquad T_x = \frac{x}{\omega} = 21.6 \; \text{ms}$$

we have the step response

$$S\left(\frac{V_x}{E_m}\right) = S(\gamma) = [10 \times 0, 0.370, 0.387, 0.403, 0.418, 0.432, 0.445,$$

$$0.457, 0.468, 0.478, 0.487, 0.495, \ldots]$$

Thus for any excitation $v(0, t)$ we may determine the sequence $S(V_x)$ by the superposition of the step responses $(S(v(0, t)) = S(V_0))$:

$$S(V_x) = S(V_0') * S(\gamma) \cong \frac{1}{\tau} S(V_0) * [1, -1] * S(\gamma)$$

CHAPTER 4 Accuracy Considerations

INTRODUCTION

The discrete-time approach for system analysis is not an exact computation approach, but gives only an approximation which depends on many factors: choice of the increment size, algorithm, and so forth.

For engineering application, it is useful to know the degree of accuracy that can be obtained by its computation and how to improve this accuracy, if necessary, at the cost of an increase in computational work. The degree of accuracy can be determined only in the case where it is possible to compute an exact solution. After some general discussion of errors and accuracy, Sec. 4.2 considers the spectral errors of integrating operators and compares the result obtained by the different types of integrating operators. Section 4.3 is related to the building of round-off and truncation errors. Section 4.4 discusses selection of the magnitude and optimal size of the independent variable increment.

4.1 ERRORS AND ACCURACY CONSIDERATIONS

In most cases, application of impulse analysis does not give the exact solution, but only an approximate solution. No general theory of the accuracy exists. However, in many cases an indication of the accuracy of a method may be obtained by performing the operation in question on a problem with known solution and comparing the results with the known solution.

This technique is frequently misleading because, if the "exact solution" is derived from the mathematical model of a physical process, errors in the model are not taken into consideration.

This situation is further complicated by the fact that an analytical solution is determined by analytical expressions for the variables of the process, which are often given by measured curves. The expressions and the curves usually do not correspond exactly. Applications of impulse analysis in many cases is more accurate than the analytical formulation, since it uses the actual values of the recorded data and not analytic approximations.

The accuracy of any numerical computation depends upon the sample interval and the computational scheme. It is evident that the accuracy increases with small increment size and more elaborate computational schemes. However, these are purchased with increased labor and greater computation time and, as will be seen in Sec. 4.3, reach a point where errors actually increase with decreased increment size.

In practice, a problem is frequently solved several times with different increment sizes, yielding a family of approximate solutions. If halving the sample interval does not appreciably change the solution, it is assumed that the approximate solution is near the exact solution. In some cases it is possible to obtain a result as a function of the sample interval and demonstrate that the result does in fact converge to the "exact solution."

Presently we rely almost entirely upon experience and intuition for determining if accuracy is to be increased by a decreased sample increment or an increased complexity of the computational scheme. Given a relationship among the labor (cost) involved in configuration complexity, the cost of increased computation time resulting from smaller increment sizes, and the cost of inaccuracies in the results, the situation is reduced to an optimization problem. Some aspects of the formulation and solution of this problem are presented in Sec. 4.4.

We shall now discuss several sources of errors in numerical calculations and their effect on the resultant calculations.

Round-off errors are due to the representation of numbers by a finite number of decimal (or binary) digits. In general, round-off errors are introduced by rounding a number to the number of significant figures carried in the calculation or those due to the limited word length of the computer. A practical technique for estimating the round-off error introduced by a technique on a particular machine is to solve a problem twice, once in single precision arithmetic and once in double precision. The difference in the solutions is a good estimate of the round-off error. This, of course, assumes that the round-off error in double precision is negligible.

Statistical analyses have been applied recently to the propagation of round-off errors. These procedures will be discussed briefly in Sec. 4.3 with regard to their effect on error buildup.

Truncation errors are due to finite approximations of limiting processes. For example, taking only a finite number of terms of a Taylor series expansion to obtain an approximation for the derivative is the "truncation" of the series and results in an inexact formula.

Numerical differentiation tends to be inaccurate in the sense that the accuracy of the derivative may be less than the accuracy of the functional values from which it was derived. Also, a polynomial can (or Taylor series expansion) approximate integrals better than it can approximate the function itself. Thus integration tends to be more accurate than interpolation, which in turn is more accurate than differentiation.

Consider the central difference formula (Eq. 2.17), taken with interval τ having the general term

$$f_n' \approx \frac{f_n^{\,v} - f_{n-1}^{\,v}}{\tau} \tag{4.1}$$

The relative error of $(f_n^{\,v} - f_{n-1}^{\,v})$ is much greater than the error of $f_n^{\,v}$ or $f_{n-1}^{\,v}$ separately when τ is small, since for small τ, $f_n^{\,v} \approx f_{n+1}^{\,v}$. Thus the increment τ should not be too small because inaccuracies in the data and round-off errors will have a great effect. However, if τ is large, the error in Eqs. (2.17) and (4.1) is large. Some insight into the selection of τ is obtained in the following example.

EXAMPLE 4.1

Consider Eq. (4.1) written as

$$f_n' = \frac{f_n^{\,v} - f_{n-1}^{\,v}}{\tau} + E_1 \tag{4.2}$$

where E_1 is the remainder, or error in Eq. (4.1).

E_1 may be estimated by expanding Eq. (4.2) in a Taylor series around $t = (n + 1)\tau$:

$$f_n^{\,v} = f_n + \tfrac{1}{2}\tau f_n' + \tfrac{1}{8}\tau^2 f_n'' + \tfrac{1}{48}\tau^3 f_n''' + \cdots$$

$$f_{n-1}^{\,v} = f_n - \tfrac{1}{2}\tau f_n' + \tfrac{1}{8}\tau^2 f_n'' - \tfrac{1}{48}\tau^3 f_n''' + \cdots$$

Substitution into Eq. (4.2) yields

$$E_1 \approx -\tfrac{1}{24}\tau^2 f_n''' \tag{4.3}$$

E_1 is the error in the evaluation of the derivative f_n' at the point $t = n\tau$ and is the error due to one step of the process. This error is called the *one-step* or *single-step* error.

TABLE 4.1

Step Response and Step-Response Errors of $H(s)$ for $\tau = 1.0$ s

Time	Exact	Tustin [45]	Boxer-Thaler [4]	Madwed [23]	First Difference	z-transform	Halijak [16]
			Step Response				
0.	0.	0.155556	0.018623	0.076628	0.346154	0.	0.
1.00	0.382995	0.581037	0.908129	0.686602	0.670118	0.694444	0.729167
2.00	0.862995	0.980634	0.604933	1.005198	0.875683	1.227238	1.196615
3.00	1.057645	1.112193	1.697787	1.078408	0.979161	1.032027	0.993951
4.00	1.081263	1.089155	0.022278	1.070604	1.019922	0.897912	0.925478
5.00	1.056211	1.046759	2.808335	1.041548	1.029348	1.061637	1.082077
6.00	1.031002	1.020727	-1.927654	1.022948	1.026121	1.093193	1.071386
7.00	1.015244	1.008502	5.963237	1.009952	1.019484	0.983488	0.978842
8.00	1.007005	1.003357	-7.299910	1.005022	1.013223	0.977749	0.995891
9.00	1.003082	1.001297	14.927706	1.001646	1.008451	1.028857	1.028648
10.00	1.001317	1.000492	-22.353864	1.001006	1.005180	1.014029	1.003467
			Step-Response Errors				
0.	—	-0.155556	-0.018623	-0.076628	-0.346154	0.	0.
1.00	—	-0.198042	-0.525134	-0.303607	-0.287123	-0.311449	-0.346172
2.00	—	-0.117639	0.258062	-0.142203	-0.012688	-0.364243	-0.333620
3.00	—	-0.054548	-0.640142	-0.020763	0.078484	0.025618	0.063694
4.00	—	-0.007892	1.058985	0.010659	0.061341	0.183351	0.155785
5.00	—	0.009452	-1.752124	0.014663	0.026863	-0.005426	0.025866
6.00	—	0.010275	2.958656	0.008054	0.004881	-0.062191	-0.040384
7.00	—	0.006742	-4.947993	0.005292	-0.004240	0.031756	0.036402
8.00	—	0.003648	8.306915	0.001983	-0.006218	0.029256	0.011114
9.00	—	0.001785	-13.924624	0.001436	-0.005369	-0.025775	-0.025566
10.00	—	0.000825	23.355181	0.000311	-0.003863	-0.012712	-0.002150
		0.007323	76.958600	0.010830	0.019381	0.024594	0.023988

TABLE 4.2

STEP RESPONSE AND STEP-RESPONSE ERRORS OF $H(s)$ FOR $\tau = 2.0$ s

Time	Exact	Tustin [45]	Boxer-Thaler [4]	Madwed [23]	First Difference	z-transform	Halijak [16]
				Step Response			
0.	−0.	0.009824	0.002173	0.005449	0.035948	0.	0.
0.20	0.020118	0.047824	0.041083	0.043084	0.100186	0.031333	0.031500
0.40	0.077711	0.118854	0.115677	0.115840	0.184095	0.095868	0.096245
0.60	0.164328	0.213996	0.214680	0.314403	0.279556	0.188623	0.189172
0.80	0.269416	0.323152	0.326795	0.324514	0.379665	0.301027	0.301665
1.00	0.382995	0.437162	0.442482	0.439949	0.478983	0.423395	0.424024
1.20	0.496866	0.548747	0.554540	0.552267	0.573525	0.546630	0.547158
1.40	0.604975	0.652722	0.658070	0.656371	0.660609	0.663242	0.663599
1.60	0.703314	0.745823	0.750150	0.749159	0.738639	0.767816	0.767959
1.80	0.789620	0.826379	0.829417	0.829126	0.806880	0.857069	0.856986
2.00	0.862995	0.893935	0.895655	0.895963	0.865243	0.929639	0.929345
2.20	0.923534	0.948898	0.949433	0.950191	0.914098	0.985719	0.985248
2.40	0.972004	0.992238	0.991810	0.992856	0.954120	1.026624	1.026023
2.60	1.009583	1.025243	1.024110	1.025293	0.986164	1.054377	1.053701
2.80	1.037650	1.049345	1.047759	1.048952	1.011171	1.071342	1.070643
3.00	1.057645	1.065985	1.064168	1.065276	1.030103	1.079929	1.079254
3.20	1.070969	1.076534	1.074668	1.075625	1.043887	1.082387	1.081775
3.40	1.078915	1.082238	1.080456	1.081227	1.053389	1.080669	1.080147
3.60	1.082639	1.084191	1.082585	1.083159	1.059398	1.076371	1.075955
3.80	1.083140	1.083330	1.081954	1.082336	1.062608	1.070716	1.070412

4.00	1.081263	1.080438	1.079315	1.079521	1.063626	1.064581	1.064386
4.20	1.077704	1.076152	1.075280	1.075338	1.062967	1.058542	1.058447
4.40	1.073025	1.070979	1.070343	1.070280	1.061064	1.052936	1.052927
4.60	1.067669	1.065316	1.064888	1.064735	1.058276	1.047916	1.047976
4.80	1.061979	1.059464	1.059213	1.058996	1.054892	1.043513	1.043626
5.00	1.056211	1.053645	1.053537	1.053281	1.051144	1.039679	1.039828
5.20	1.050551	1.048017	1.048020	1.047746	1.047214	1.036327	1.036497
5.40	1.045132	1.042687	1.042771	1.042496	1.043242	1.033356	1.033535
5.60	1.040037	1.037722	1.037862	1.037598	1.039332	1.030673	1.030852
5.80	1.040037	1.03772	1.037862	1.037598	1.035559	1.028200	1.028371
6.00	1.031002	1.029011	1.029201	1.028983	1.031976	1.025879	1.026037
6.20	1.027093	1.025275	1.025468	1.025280	1.028617	1.023671	1.023815
6.40	1.023583	1.021938	1.022124	1.021967	1.025501	1.021558	1.021686
6.60	1.020454	1.018977	1.019149	1.019022	1.022637	1.019534	1.019645
6.80	1.017684	1.016365	1.016519	1.016421	1.020024	1.017600	1.017696
7.00	1.015255	1.014073	1.014207	1.014135	1.017656	1.015767	1.015849
7.20	1.013106	1.012071	1.012184	1.012136	1.015523	1.014043	1.014113
7.40	1.011241	1.010330	1.010423	1.010394	1.013611	1.012439	1.012498
7.60	1.009620	1.008821	1.008894	1.008884	1.011905	1.010961	1.011012
7.80	1.008216	1.007517	1.007574	1.007577	1.010389	1.009615	1.009657
8.00	1.007005	1.006395	1.006436	1.006450	1.009048	1.008398	1.008434
8.20	1.005961	1.005431	1.005458	1.005482	1.007864	1.007310	1.007339
8.40	1.005065	1.004605	1.004621	1.004651	1.006822	1.006344	1.006367
8.60	1.004298	1.003899	1.003906	1.003940	1.005909	1.005492	1.005510
8.80	1.003642	1.003296	1.003296	1.003333	1.005110	1.004744	1.004758

(continued)

TABLE 4.2—*(continued)*

Time	Exact	Tustin [45]	Boxer-Thaler [4]	Madwed [23]	First Difference	z-transform	Halijak [16]
9.00	1.003082	1.002783	1.002771	1.002815	1.004412	1.004092	1.004102
9.20	1.002606	1.002347	1.002337	1.002375	1.003804	1.003524	1.003530
9.40	1.002200	1.001977	1.001963	1.002001	1.003275	1.003030	1.003034
9.60	1.001856	1.001663	1.001647	1.001683	1.002816	1.002602	1.002603
9.80	1.001564	1.001397	1.001380	1.001414	1.002419	1.002231	1.002229
10.00	1.001317	1.001173	1.001154	1.001187	1.002075	1.001909	1.001906
Step Response Errors							
0		−0.009824	−0.002173	−0.005449	−0.035948	−0	−0.
0.20		−0.027724	−0.020965	−0.022966	−0.080068	−0.011215	−0.011382
0.40		−0.041143	−0.037966	−0.038129	−0.106382	−0.018157	−0.018534
0.60		−0.049668	−0.050352	−0.048975	−0.115228	−0.024295	−0.024844
0.80		−0.053736	−0.057379	−0.055098	−0.110249	−0.031611	−0.032249
1.00		−0.054167	−0.059487	−0.056954	−0.095988	−0.040400	−0.041029
1.20		−0.051881	−0.057674	−0.055401	−0.076659	−0.049764	−0.050292
1.40		−0.047747	−0.053095	−0.051396	−0.055634	−0.058267	−0.058624
1.60		−0.042509	−0.046836	−0.045845	−0.064502	−0.064645	−0.000002
1.80		−0.036759	−0.039797	−0.039506	−0.017260	−0.067449	−0.067366
2.00		−0.030940	−0.032660	−0.032968	−0.002248	−0.066644	−0.066350
2.20		−0.025364	−0.025899	−0.026657	0.009436	−0.062185	−0.061714
2.40		−0.020234	−0.019806	−0.020852	0.017884	−0.054620	−0.054019
2.60		−0.015660	−0.014527	−0.015710	0.023419	−0.044794	−0.044118
2.80		−0.011695	−0.010109	−0.011302	0.026479	−0.033692	−0.032993

3.00	−0.003340	−0.006523	−0.007631	0.027542	−0.022284	−0.021609
3.20	−0.005565	−0.003699	−0.004656	0.027082	−0.011418	−0.010806
3.40	−0.003323	−0.001541	−0.002312	0.025526	−0.001754	−0.001232
3.60	−0.001552	0.000054	−0.000520	0.023241	0.006268	0.006684
3.80	−0.000190	0.001186	0.000804	0.020532	0.012424	0.012728
4.00	0.000825	0.001948	0.001742	0.017637	0.016682	0.016877
4.20	0.001552	0.002424	0.002366	0.014737	0.019162	0.019257
4.40	0.002046	0.002682	0.002745	0.011961	0.020098	0.020098
4.60	0.002353	0.002781	0.002934	0.009393	0.919753	0.019693
4.80	0.002515	0.002766	0.002983	0.007087	0.018466	0.018353
5.00	0.002566	0.002674	0.002930	0.005067	0.016532	0.016383
5.20	0.002534	0.002531	0.002805	0.003337	0.014224	0.014054
5.40	0.002445	0.002361	0.002636	0.001890	0.011776	0.011597
5.60	0.002315	0.002175	0.002439	0.000705	0.009364	0.009185
5.80	0.002160	0.001987	0.002230	−0.000240	0.007119	0.006948
6.00	0.001991	0.001801	0.002019	−0.000974	0.005123	0.004965
6.20	0.001818	0.001625	0.001813	−0.001524	0.003422	0.003278
6.40	0.001645	0.001459	0.001616	−0.001918	0.002025	0.001897
6.60	0.001477	0.001305	0.001432	−0.002183	0.000920	0.000809
6.80	0.001319	0.001165	0.001263	−0.002340	0.000084	−0.000012
7.00	0.001171	0.001037	0.001109	−0.002412	−0.000523	−0.000605
7.20	0.001035	0.000922	0.000970	−0.002417	−0.000937	−0.001007
7.40	0.000911	0.000818	0.000847	−0.002370	−0.001198	−0.001257
7.60	0.000799	0.000726	0.000736	−0.002285	−0.001341	−0.001392
7.80	0.000699	0.000642	0.000639	−0.002173	−0.001399	−0.001441

(continued)

TABLE 4.2—(*continued*)

Time	Exact	Tustin [45]	Boxer-Thaler [4]	Madwed [23]	First Difference	z-transform	Halijak [16]
8.00		0.000610	0.000569	0.000555	-0.002043	-0.001393	-0.001429
8.20		0.000530	0.000503	0.000479	-0.001903	-0.001349	-0.001378
8.40		0.000460	0.000444	0.000414	-0.001757	-0.001279	-0.001302
8.60		0.000399	0.000392	0.000358	-0.001611	-0.001194	-0.001212
8.80		0.000346	0.000346	0.000309	-0.001468	-0.001102	-0.001116
9.00		0.000299	0.000305	0.000267	-0.001330	-0.001010	-0.001020
9.20		0.000259	0.000269	0.000231	-0.001198	-0.000918	-0.000924
9.40		0.000223	0.000237	0.000199	-0.001075	-0.000830	-0.000834
9.60		0.000193	0.000209	0.000173	-0.000960	-0.000746	-0.000747
9.80		0.000167	0.000184	0.000150	-0.000855	-0.000667	-0.000665
10.00		0.000144	0.000163	0.000130	-0.000758	-0.000592	-0.000589
		0.000423	0.000466	0.000448	0.001370	0.000708	0.000706

The truncation and round-off errors are bound to accumulate in step-by-step procedures because the starting point at each step is incorrect and each step introduces new errors. This accumulation is called *error buildup*.

The interaction of the truncation and round-off errors is investigated in Problem 4.1 (Appendix).

EXAMPLE 4.2†

The transfer function

$$H(s) = \frac{s^2 + 5.5s + 2.5}{s^4 + 5s^3 + 9.5s^2 + 8s + 2.5} \tag{4.4}$$

is to be simulated by several of the z-form integrating substitutions given in Table 2.13 and the step response and step-response errors tabulated in Tables 4.1 and 4.2.

First, the numerator and denominator of $H(s)$ is divided through by $1/s^4$, yielding

$$H(s) = \frac{(1/s^2) + 5.5(1/s^3) + 2.5(1/s^4)}{1 + 5(1/s) + 9.5(1/s^2) + 8(1/s^3) + 2.5(1/s^4)} \tag{4.5}$$

The z-forms of Table 2.13 are substituted into Eq. (4.5) to yield (for the Tustin operators) the recursion relation

$$
\begin{aligned}
Y_n = \{ & (2.5T^4 + 11T^3 + 4T^2)X + (10T^4 + 22T^3)X_{n-1} \\
& + (15T^4 - 8T^2)X_{n-2} + (10T^4 - 22T^3)X_{n-3} \\
& + (2.5T^4 - 11T^3 + 4T^2)X_{n-4} \\
& + (-10T^4 - 32T^3 + 80T + 64)Y_{n-1} + (-15T^4 + 76T^2 - 96)Y_{n-2} \\
& + (-10T^4 + 32T^3 - 80T + 64)Y_{n-1} + (-25T^4 + 16T^3 - 38T^2 \\
& + (40T - 16)Y_{n-4} \} \left\{ \frac{1}{25T^4 + 16T^3 + 38T^2 + 40T + 16} \right\} \tag{4.6}
\end{aligned}
$$

Tables 4.1 and 4.2 give the resultant step response and step-response errors for $\tau = 0.2$ s and $\tau = 1$ s, respectively. Note that for the smaller increment size, the errors are considerably smaller. Of particular interest is the instability of the Boxer-Thaler [4] technique with $\tau = 1$ s, and its stability and good accuracy with $\tau = 0.2$ s.

This phenomenon points out that if τ is too large, the response of the discrete approximation may bear no relation to the response of the original

---

† From Rosko [37].

system. In this case, if τ is too large, the discrete approximation of the system has a reponse that grows exponentially in magnitude and alternates in sign. This phenomenon should not be confused with instability due to the discrete equations' possessing solutions in addition to the approximate solutions to the system equations. This phenomenon will be investigated in the next section.

4.2 SPECTRAL ERRORS OF INTEGRATING OPERATORS

In this section we develop the truncation error of several integrating operators in terms of the frequency content of the signals relative to the sampling frequency. This section follows the development of Rosko [36].

The ideal integrator has the frequency characteristic

$$\lim_{s \to j\omega} \left(\frac{1}{s^n}\right) = \left(\frac{1}{j\omega}\right)^n \tag{4.7}$$

Consider the third-order z-transform operator:

$$\left(\frac{1}{s}\right)^3 \to \frac{\tau^3}{2} \frac{z^2 + z}{(z - 1)^3} \tag{4.8}$$

Setting $z = e^{j\omega t}$, we have

$$\left(\frac{1}{s}\right)^3 \to \frac{j\tau^3}{8} \frac{\cos(\omega\tau/2)}{\sin^3(\omega\tau/2)} \tag{4.9}$$

The amplitude and phase of Eq. (4.9) are

$$\text{Amplitude} = \frac{\tau^3}{8} \frac{\cos(\omega\tau/2)}{\sin^3(\omega\tau/2)}$$

$$\text{Phase} = \frac{\pi}{2}$$

Thus Eq. (4.9) is identical to a third-order integrator in phase and closely approximates $(1/s)^3$ in amplitude τ, since

$$\frac{j\tau^3}{8} \frac{\cos(\omega\tau/2)}{\sin^3(\omega\tau/2)} = \frac{j}{\omega^3} - \frac{j\omega^4}{240} - \frac{j\omega^3\tau^6}{3024} + \cdots \approx \frac{1}{(j\omega)^3} \tag{4.10}$$

for small τ.

Rosko [37] has tabulated several integrating operators in the closed form and series form representations of Eqs. (4.9) and (4.10). These frequency characteristics appear in Table 4.3.

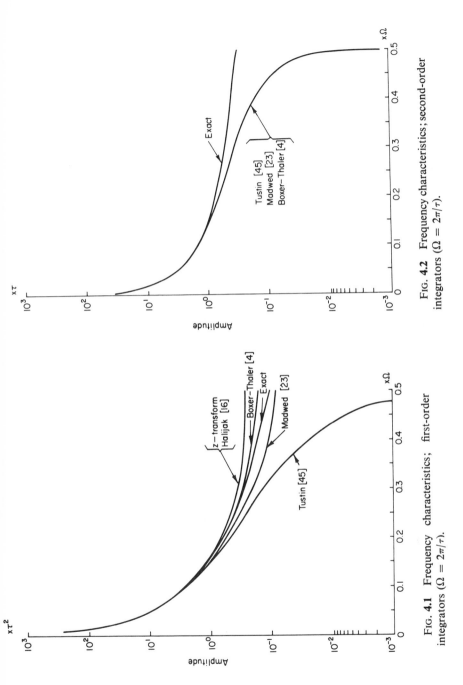

FIG. **4.2** Frequency characteristics; second-order integrators ($\Omega = 2\pi/\tau$).

FIG. **4.1** Frequency characteristics; first-order integrators ($\Omega = 2\pi/\tau$).

117

TABLE 4.3

FREQUENCY CHARACTERISTICS OF APPROXIMATE INTEGRATING OPERATORS

Method and integrating order	Closed expansion	Series expansion	Amplitude	Phase
Exact				
$\int$	$\dfrac{-j}{\omega}$	—	$\dfrac{1}{\omega}$	$-\dfrac{\pi}{2}$
$\int\int$	$\dfrac{-1}{\omega^2}$	—	$\dfrac{1}{\omega^2}$	$-\pi$
$\int\int\int$	$\dfrac{j}{\omega^3}$	—	$\dfrac{1}{\omega^3}$	$\dfrac{\pi}{2}$
$\int\int\int\int$	$\dfrac{1}{\omega^4}$	—	$\dfrac{1}{\omega^4}$	0
Tustin [45]				
$\int$	$\dfrac{-j\tau}{2}\cot\left(\dfrac{\omega\tau}{2}\right)$	$\dfrac{-j}{\omega} + \dfrac{j\omega\tau^2}{12} + \dfrac{\omega^3\tau^4}{720} + \dfrac{j\omega^5\tau^6}{30{,}240} + \cdots$	$\left|\dfrac{\tau}{2}\cot\left(\dfrac{\omega\tau}{2}\right)\right|$	$-\dfrac{\pi}{2}$
$\int\int$	$\dfrac{-\tau^2}{4}\cot^2\left(\dfrac{\omega\tau}{2}\right)$	$\dfrac{-1}{\omega^2} + \dfrac{\tau^2}{6} - \dfrac{\omega^2\tau^4}{240} - \dfrac{\omega^4\tau^6}{6048} + \cdots$	$\dfrac{\tau^2}{4}\cot^2\left(\dfrac{\omega\tau}{2}\right)$	$-\pi$
$\int\int\int$	$\dfrac{j\tau^3}{8}\cot^3\left(\dfrac{\omega\tau}{2}\right)$	$\dfrac{j}{\omega^3} - \dfrac{\tau^2}{4\omega} + \dfrac{j\omega\tau^4}{60} + \dfrac{j\omega^3\tau^6}{60{,}480} + \cdots$	$\left|\dfrac{\tau^3}{8}\cot^3\left(\dfrac{\omega\tau}{2}\right)\right|$	$\dfrac{\pi}{2}$
$\int\int\int\int$	$\dfrac{\tau^4}{16}\cot^4\left(\dfrac{\omega\tau}{2}\right)$	$\dfrac{1}{\omega^4} - \dfrac{\tau^2}{3\omega^2} + \dfrac{13\tau^4}{360} + \dfrac{\omega^2\tau^6}{945} + \cdots$	$\dfrac{\tau^4}{16}\cot^4\left(\dfrac{\omega\tau}{2}\right)$	0

Boxer-Thaler [4]

	Closed form	Series expansion	Magnitude form	
$\displaystyle\int$	$\dfrac{-j\tau}{2}\cot\left(\dfrac{\omega\tau}{2}\right)$	$\dfrac{-j}{\omega} + \dfrac{j\omega\tau^2}{12} + \dfrac{j\omega^3\tau^4}{720} + \dfrac{j\omega^5\tau^6}{30{,}240} + \cdots$	$\left\|\dfrac{\tau}{2}\cot\left(\dfrac{\omega\tau}{2}\right)\right\|$	$-\dfrac{\pi}{2}$
$\displaystyle\int\!\!\int$	$\tau^2\!\left(\dfrac{1}{12} - \dfrac{1}{4}\csc^2\left(\dfrac{\omega\tau}{2}\right)\right)$	$\dfrac{-1}{\omega^2} - \dfrac{\omega^2\tau^4}{240} - \dfrac{\omega^4\tau^6}{6048} + \cdots$	$\dfrac{\tau^2}{4}\left(\csc^2\left(\dfrac{\omega\tau}{2}\right) - \dfrac{1}{3}\right)$	$-\pi$
$\displaystyle\int\!\!\int\!\!\int$	$\dfrac{j\tau^3}{8}\cdot\dfrac{\cos(\omega\tau/2)}{\sin^3(\omega\tau/2)}$	$\dfrac{j}{\omega^3} - \dfrac{j\omega\tau^4}{240} - \dfrac{j\omega^3\tau^6}{3024} + \cdots$	$\left\|\dfrac{\tau^3}{8}\cdot\dfrac{\cos(\omega\tau/2)}{\sin^3(\omega\tau/2)}\right\|$	$\dfrac{\pi}{2}$
$\displaystyle\int\!\!\int\!\!\int\!\!\int$	$\dfrac{\tau^4}{48}\left(\dfrac{2+\cos(\omega\tau)}{\sin^4(\omega\tau/2)} - \dfrac{1}{15}\right)$	$\dfrac{1}{\omega^4} + \dfrac{\omega^2\tau^5}{3024} + \dfrac{\omega^4\tau^8}{34{,}560} + \cdots$	$\dfrac{\tau^4}{48}\left(\dfrac{2+\cos(\omega\tau)}{\sin^4(\omega\tau/2)} - \dfrac{1}{15}\right)$	0

Madwed [23]

	Closed form	Series expansion	Magnitude form	
$\displaystyle\int$	$\dfrac{-j\tau}{2}\cot\left(\dfrac{\omega\tau}{2}\right)$	$\dfrac{-j}{\omega} + \dfrac{j\omega\tau^2}{12} + \dfrac{j\omega^3\tau^4}{720} + \dfrac{j\omega^5\tau^6}{30{,}240} + \cdots$	$\left\|\dfrac{\tau}{2}\cot\left(\dfrac{\omega\tau}{2}\right)\right\|$	$-\dfrac{\pi}{2}$
$\displaystyle\int\!\!\int$	$\tau^2\!\left(\dfrac{1}{6} - \dfrac{1}{4}\csc^2\left(\dfrac{\omega\tau}{2}\right)\right)$	$\dfrac{-1}{\omega^2} + \dfrac{\tau^2}{12} - \dfrac{\omega^2\tau^4}{240} - \dfrac{\omega^4\tau^6}{6048} + \cdots$	$\dfrac{\tau^2}{2}\left(\dfrac{1}{2}\csc^2\left(\dfrac{\omega\tau}{2}\right) - \dfrac{1}{3}\right)$	$-\pi$
$\displaystyle\int\!\!\int\!\!\int$	$\dfrac{j\tau^3}{24}\cot^3\left(\dfrac{\omega\tau}{2}\right)\left[1 + 2\sec^2\left(\dfrac{\omega\tau}{2}\right)\right]$	$\dfrac{j}{\omega^3} - \dfrac{j\tau^2}{12\omega} + \dfrac{j\omega\tau^4}{360} - \dfrac{j13\omega^3\tau^6}{60{,}480} + \cdots$	$\dfrac{\tau^3}{24}\left\|\cot^3\left(\dfrac{\omega\tau}{2}\right)\right\|\left[1 + 2\sec^2\left(\dfrac{\omega\tau}{2}\right)\right]$	$\dfrac{\pi}{2}$
$\displaystyle\int\!\!\int\!\!\int\!\!\int$	$\dfrac{\tau^4}{480}\csc^4\left(\dfrac{\omega\tau}{2}\right)\left[4\cos^4\left(\dfrac{\omega\tau}{2}\right)\right.$ $\left.+\, 11\cos(\omega\tau) + 15\right]$	$\dfrac{1}{\omega^4} - \dfrac{\tau^2}{12\omega^2} + \dfrac{\tau^4}{360} - \dfrac{\omega^2\tau^6}{60{,}480} + \cdots$	$\dfrac{\tau^4}{480}\csc^4\left(\dfrac{\omega\tau}{2}\right)\left[4\cos^4\left(\dfrac{\omega\tau}{2}\right)\right.$ $\left.+\, 11\cos(\omega\tau) + 15\right]$	0

(continued)

TABLE 4.3—continued

Method and integrating order	Closed expansion	Series expansion	Amplitude	Phase
First difference				
$\int$	$\frac{\tau}{2}\left(1 - j\cot\left(\frac{\omega\tau}{2}\right)\right)$	$\frac{-j}{\omega} + \frac{\tau}{2} + \frac{j\omega\tau^2}{12} + \frac{j\omega^3\tau^4}{720} + \frac{j\omega^5\tau^6}{30,240} + \cdots$	$\frac{\tau}{2}\left\lvert\csc\left(\frac{\omega\tau}{2}\right)\right\rvert$	$-\frac{\pi}{2} + \left(\frac{\pi}{\Omega}\right)\omega$
$\int\int$	$\frac{\tau^2}{4}\left(1 - j\cot\left(\frac{\omega\tau}{2}\right)\right)^2$	$\frac{-1}{\omega^2} - \frac{j\tau}{\omega} + \frac{5\tau^2}{12} + \frac{j\omega\tau^3}{12} - \frac{\omega^2\tau^4}{240} + \frac{j\omega^3\tau^5}{720} + \cdots$	$\frac{\tau^2}{4}\csc^2\left(\frac{\omega\tau}{2}\right)$	$-\pi + \left(\frac{2\pi}{\Omega}\right)\omega$
$\int\int\int$	$\frac{\tau^3}{8}\left(1 - j\cot\left(\frac{\omega\tau}{2}\right)\right)^3$	$\frac{j}{\omega^3} - \frac{3}{2}\frac{\tau}{\omega^2} - \frac{j\tau^2}{\omega} + \frac{3}{8}\tau^3 + \frac{j57\omega\tau^4}{720} - \frac{\omega^2\tau^5}{160} + \cdots$	$\frac{\tau^3}{8}\left\lvert\csc^3\left(\frac{\omega\tau}{2}\right)\right\rvert$	$-\frac{3\pi}{2} + \left(\frac{3\pi}{\Omega}\right)\omega$
$\int\int\int\int$	$\frac{\tau^4}{16}\left(1 - j\cot\left(\frac{\omega\tau}{2}\right)\right)^4$	$\frac{1}{\omega^4} + \frac{j2\tau}{\omega^3} - \frac{11}{6}\frac{\tau^2}{\omega^2} - \frac{j\tau^3}{\omega} + \frac{221}{720}\tau^4 + \frac{j3\omega\tau^5}{40} + \cdots$	$\frac{\tau^4}{16}\csc^4\left(\frac{\omega\tau}{2}\right)$	$\left(\frac{4\pi}{\Omega}\right)\omega$
z-transform				
$\int$	$\frac{\tau}{2}\left(1 - j\cot\left(\frac{\omega\tau}{2}\right)\right)$	$\frac{-j}{\omega} + \frac{\tau}{2} + \frac{j\omega\tau^2}{12} + \frac{j\omega^3\tau^4}{720} + \frac{j\omega^5\tau^6}{30,240} + \cdots$	$\frac{\tau}{2}\left\lvert\csc\left(\frac{\omega\tau}{2}\right)\right\rvert$	$-\frac{\pi}{2} + \left(\frac{\pi}{\Omega}\right)\omega$
$\int\int$	$-\frac{\tau^2}{4}\csc^2\left(\frac{\omega\tau}{2}\right)$	$\frac{-1}{\omega^2} - \frac{\tau^2}{12} - \frac{\omega^2\tau^4}{240} - \frac{\omega^4\tau^6}{6048} + \cdots$	$\frac{\tau^2}{4}\csc^2\left(\frac{\omega\tau}{2}\right)$	$-\pi$
$\int\int\int$	$\frac{j\tau^3}{8}\frac{\cos(\omega\tau/2)}{\sin^3(\omega\tau/2)}$	$\frac{j}{\omega^3} - \frac{j\omega\tau^4}{240} - \frac{j\omega^3\tau^6}{3024} + \cdots$	$\left\lvert\frac{\tau^3}{8}\frac{\cos(\omega\tau/2)}{\sin^3(\omega\tau/2)}\right\rvert$	$\frac{\pi}{2}$
$\int\int\int\int$	$\frac{\tau^4}{48}\left(\frac{2 + \cos(\omega\tau)}{\sin^4(\omega\tau/2)}\right)$	$\frac{1}{\omega^4} + \frac{\tau^4}{720} + \frac{\omega^2\tau^6}{3024} + \cdots$	$\frac{\tau^4}{48}\left(\frac{2 + \cos(\omega\tau)}{\sin^4(\omega\tau/2)}\right)$	0

Halijack [16]

$\int$	$\dfrac{\tau}{2}\left(1 - j\cot\left(\dfrac{\omega\tau}{2}\right)\right)$	$\dfrac{-j}{\omega} + \dfrac{\tau}{2} + \dfrac{j\omega\tau^2}{12} + \dfrac{j\omega^3\tau^4}{720} + \dfrac{j\omega^5\tau^6}{30,240} + \cdots$	$\dfrac{\tau}{2}\left|\csc\left(\dfrac{\omega\tau}{2}\right)\right|$	$\dfrac{-\pi}{2} + \left(\dfrac{\pi}{\Omega}\right)\omega$
$\int\int$	$\dfrac{-\tau^2}{4}\csc^2\left(\dfrac{\omega\tau}{2}\right)$	$\dfrac{-1}{\omega^2} - \dfrac{\tau^2}{12} - \dfrac{\omega^2\tau^4}{240} - \dfrac{\omega^4\tau^6}{6048} + \cdots$	$\dfrac{\tau^2}{4}\csc^2\left(\dfrac{\omega\tau}{2}\right)$	$-\pi$
$\int\int\int$	$\dfrac{j\tau^3}{8}\left(\dfrac{\cos\omega\tau/2}{\sin^3(\omega\tau/2)}\right)$	$\dfrac{j}{\omega^3} - \dfrac{j\omega\tau^4}{240} - \dfrac{j\omega^3\tau^6}{3024} + \cdots$	$\left|\dfrac{\tau^3}{8}\cdot\dfrac{\cos(\omega\tau/2)}{\sin^3(\omega\tau/2)}\right|$	$\dfrac{\pi}{2}$
$\int\int\int\int$	$\dfrac{\tau^4}{32}\left(\dfrac{1+\cos(\omega\tau)}{\sin^4(\omega\tau/2)}\right)$	$\dfrac{1}{\omega^4} - \dfrac{\tau^2}{12\omega^2} - \dfrac{\tau^4}{180} - \dfrac{\omega^2\tau^6}{1728} + \cdots$	$\dfrac{\tau^4}{32}\csc^4\left[\dfrac{\omega\tau}{2}\right][\cos(\omega\tau) + 1]$	0

NOTES: (1) τ = sampling period in seconds. (2) $\Omega = 2\pi/\tau$; angular sampling frequency. (3) The phase characteristic is that which is applicable to the usable low-pass region; that is, $\omega \leq \pi/\tau$.

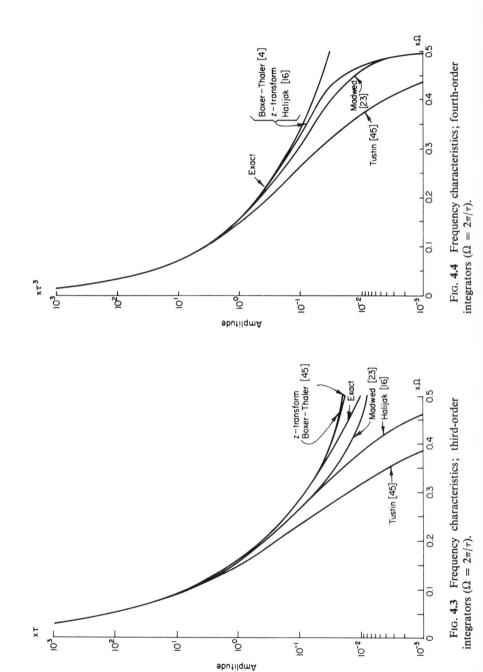

FIG. **4.4** Frequency characteristics; fourth-order integrators ($\Omega = 2\pi/\tau$).

FIG. **4.3** Frequency characteristics; third-order integrators ($\Omega = 2\pi/\tau$).

122

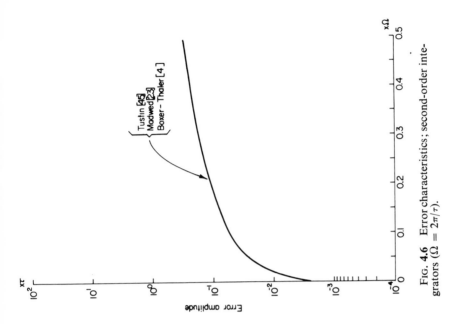

FIG. 4.6 Error characteristics; second-order integrators ($\Omega = 2\pi/\tau$).

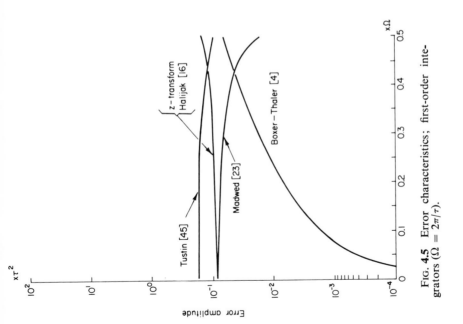

FIG. 4.5 Error characteristics; first-order integrators ($\Omega = 2\pi/\tau$).

123

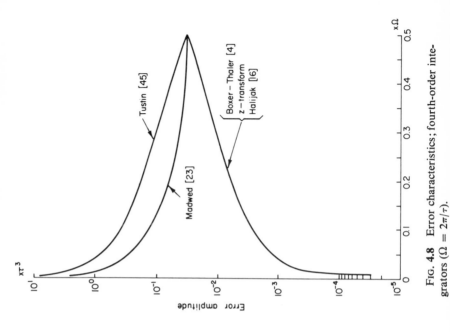

FIG. **4.8** Error characteristics; fourth-order integrators ($\Omega = 2\pi/\tau$).

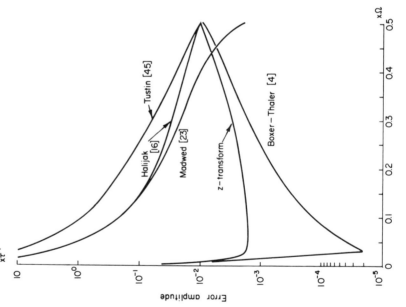

FIG. **4.7** Error characteristics; third-order integrators ($\Omega = 2\pi/\tau$).

124

Figures 4.1 through 4.4 are plots of the amplitude characteristics of the substitutional integrators given in Table 4.3, along with the ideal integrator amplitude characteristics. Defining the spectral error to be the difference between the ideal integrator and the three-form substitutional integrator, we have

$$E_n(j\omega) = \frac{1}{(j\omega)^n} - H_n(j\omega) \qquad (4.11)$$

where $H_n(j\omega)$ is the frequency characteristic of the operator. This difference may be evaluated from Table 4.3. Figures 4.5 through 4.8 show the amplitude of the spectral error for the integrating operators in Table 4.1.

These error characteristics and Table 4.3 will be utilized in Sec. 4.4 for the optimum selection of the independent variable increment τ.

4.3 ERROR BUILDUP

The buildup of errors in numerical calculations is of utmost concern. Truncation errors are generally greatest for large increment sizes, and round-off errors are most significant for small increments and a large number of operations. Frequently, round-off errors build up statistically and grow like the square root of the number of steps. However, once introduced, the effect of a single error may die out so that only the last few errors matter, or it may grow exponentially, cause instability, and eventually dominate the solution.

In this section we shall first look at the buildup of round-off errors, then examine truncation errors, and conclude with application to several examples.

4.3.1 Round-off Errors

If the maximum round-off error per step is less than ϵ, then after n steps of a calculation the maximum error is less than $n\epsilon$. This situation is analogous to the estimates of the maximum effect of inaccurate data and gives a pessimistic estimate of the total error, as will be seen below.

Suppose that the cumulative round-off error $e_n = e(n\tau)$ is the weighted sum of the per-step round-off errors δ_i ($i = 1, 2, \ldots, n$):

$$e_n = \sum_{i=1}^{n} d_i \, \delta_i \qquad (4.12)$$

where the d_i are the weights of the individual round-off errors.

If the δ_i are independent random variables† with means μ_i and standard deviations σ_i, the mean and standard deviation of the random quantity [Eq. (4.12)] are

$$\mu = \sum_{i=1}^{N} d_i\mu_i \quad \text{and} \quad \sigma^2 = \sum_{i=1}^{N} d_i^2\sigma_i^2 \tag{4.13}$$

If the round-off errors δ_i are uniformly distributed in the interval $-\epsilon \leq \delta_i \leq \epsilon$, then $\sigma_i = \epsilon/3$, and if the d_i are unity,

$$\mu = 0 \quad \text{and} \quad \sigma = \frac{\epsilon}{\sqrt{3}}\sqrt{n}$$

by Eq. (4.13). Thus, as the increment τ decreases, the standard deviation of the cumulative round-off error increases inversely as $\sqrt{\tau}$, and the maximum possible error $(n\epsilon)$ increases inversely as τ.

For large n, e_n approaches a Gaussian distribution and there is only 0.05 probability that e_n will exceed 2σ. For $n = 100$, then, the maximum error $|e_n| \leq 100\epsilon$, while $2\sigma \approx 11.5\epsilon$ so that it is unlikely that the error will be greater than one-tenth of the pessimistic estimate.

The preceding discussion does not consider the effect of an error once it has been introduced. It has been assumed that the round-off errors build up in an additive fashion. This is generally not the case, as will be seen below. One technique for estimating the effects of round-off errors is to intentionally perturb the solution by the addition of one digit in the last significant place at every stage of the calculation. This exaggerates the round-off errors and gives a high estimate.

Another technique for estimating the round-off error is to run the problem on the computer twice: once in single precision and once in double precision, the assumption being that the round-off error is negligible in double precision.

Finally, solutions that are particularly sensitive to small changes in initial conditions will normally be sensitive to roundoff errors. Therefore, if small changes in initial conditions give only small changes in response, round-off errors probably may be assumed to grow like $1/\sqrt{\tau}$.

For the differential equation

$$y' = f(y, t), \qquad y(0) = y_0 \tag{4.14}$$

---

† If $\delta_1, \delta_2, \ldots$ are observed values of a random variable,

$$\mu = \lim_{N \to \infty} \frac{1}{N} \sum_{k=1}^{N} \delta_k \quad \text{and} \quad \sigma^2 = \lim_{N \to \infty} \frac{1}{N} \sum_{k=1}^{N} (\delta_k - \mu)^2$$

by back difference we have the approximate relation

$$\frac{z_{n+1} - z_n}{\tau} = g_n, \qquad z_{n+1} = z_n + \tau g_n \qquad (n = 0, 1, 2, 3, \ldots) \qquad (4.15)$$

where $y_n = y(n\tau)$ is the exact solution of Eq. (4.14), z_n is the numerical solution obtained from Eq. (4.15), $f_n = f(y_n, n\tau)$, and $g_n = f(z_n, n\tau)$. We shall investigate the truncation error and its propagation by the analysis of Eq. (4.15).

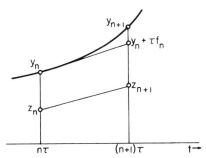

FIG. **4.9** Error buildup.

Taylor's theorem with remainder gives

$$y_{n+1} = y_n + \tau y'_n + \frac{\tau^2}{2} y''(\theta_n) \qquad (4.16)$$

where $t_n \leq \theta_n \leq t_{n+1}$ and $(\tau^2/2)y''(\theta_n)$ is the one-stage discretization, or truncation error:

$$e_{n+1} = y_{n+1} - (y_n + \tau f_n) \qquad (4.17)$$

(See Fig. 4.9.)

The total accumulated error is

$$E_n = y_n - z_n \qquad (4.18)$$

Combining Eqs. (4.15) and (4.16), we have

$$(y_{n+1} - y_n) - (z_{n+1} - z_n) = \tau f_n + e_{n+1} - \tau g_n$$

or

$$(y_{n+1} - z_{n+1}) = (y_n - z_n) + \tau(f_n - g_n) + e_{n+1}$$

Thus

$$E_{n+1} = E_n + \tau(f_n - g_n) + e_{n+1} \qquad (4.19)$$

The term $\tau(f_n - g_n)$ is the error in the $(n + 1)$th step due to E_n. Alternatively, Eqs. (4.15), (4.16), and (4.18) may be combined to give

$$E_{n+1} = E_n + \tau[f_n - g_n] - \frac{\tau^2}{2} y''(\theta_n) \qquad (4.20)$$

where $n\tau \le \theta_n \le (n + 1)\tau$ which is identical to Eq. (4.19).

By the mean value theorem,

$$f_n - g_n = f_y(\bar{y}_n, n\tau)[y_n - z_n]$$
$$= f_y(\bar{y}_n, n\tau)E_n$$

where $\bar{y}_n$ is between y_n and z_n and

$$f_y(y, t) = \frac{\partial f(y, t)}{\partial y}$$

Thus Eq. (4.20) is

$$E_{n+1} = E_n + \tau f_y(\bar{y}_n, n\tau)E_n + e_{n+1}$$

$$= E_n + \tau f_y(\bar{y}_n, n\tau)E_n - \frac{\tau^3}{2} y''(\theta_n) \qquad (4.21)$$

Suppose $|f_y(y, t)| \le A$ and $|y''(t)| \le B$. Then

$$|E_{n+1}| \le |E_n| + \tau A|E_n| + \frac{\tau^2}{2} B = (1 + \tau A)|E_n| + \frac{\tau^2 B}{2} \qquad (4.22)$$

A pessimistic estimate of the total error is the solution to the boundary formula of Eq. (4.22):

$$P_{n+1} = (1 + \tau A)P_n + \frac{\tau^2}{2} B \qquad (4.23)$$

For $P_0 = E_0 = 0$, we have $P_n \ge |E_n|$ by induction from Eq. (4.22).

The solution of Eq. (4.23) is (see Bellman and Cooke [2])

$$P_n = \frac{\tau B}{2A} (1 + \tau A)^n - \frac{\tau B}{2A} \qquad (4.24)$$

Since $P_0 = 0$ and $(1 + \tau A)^n \le e^{n\tau A}$ for $n\tau A \ge 0$,

$$P_n \le \frac{\tau B}{2A} (e^{n\tau A} - 1) \qquad (4.25)$$

thus providing an upper bound on the truncation error.

EXAMPLE 4.3†

We wish to find the value of y at $x = 1$ for the initial value problem, where

$$\frac{dy}{dt} = f(y, t) = -y, \qquad y_0 = 1 \text{ at } t = 0 \tag{4.26}$$

Using the back difference of Eq. (4.15) and $\tau = 0.001$, we can compare the answer with the analytic solution and obtain the *actual error*, which in turn can then be contrasted to the total error E_n.

From Eq. (4.16) we have the approximation

$$e_i = \frac{\tau^2}{2}\left(\frac{d^2 y}{dt^2}\right)_{t = \theta_n} \approx \frac{\tau^2}{2}\left(\frac{d^2 y}{dt^2}\right)_{t = (n-1)\tau}$$

where $((n-1)\tau \le \theta_n \le n\tau)$.

Using the given conditions in Eq. (4.26),

$$e_i = \frac{\tau^2}{2}\left[\frac{d}{dt}\left(\frac{dy}{dt}\right)_{t = (n-1)\tau}\right] = \frac{\tau^2}{2}\frac{d}{dt}(-y)_{t = (n-1)\tau} = \frac{\tau^2 z_{n-1}}{2} \tag{4.27}$$

To obtain an expression for z_{n-1} in terms of the given initial condition, we can apply the finite difference formula of Eq. (4.15):

$$z_1 = y_0 + \tau(-y_0) = y_0(1 - \tau)$$
$$z_2 = z_1 + \tau(-z_1)$$
$$= z_1(1 - \tau) = y_0(1 - \tau)^2$$
$$z_3 = y_0(1 - \tau)^3$$
$$\vdots$$
$$z_{i-1} = y_0(1 - \tau)^{i-1}$$

Substituting this expression into Eq. (4.27), we obtain

$$e_i = y_0(1 - \tau)^{i-1}\frac{\tau^2}{2} \tag{4.28}$$

By Eq. (4.26),

$$f_y(\bar{y}_m, m\tau)E_m \approx \frac{d}{dy}(-y)_{t = m\tau} E_m = -E_m$$

---

† Reprinted by permission from S. S. Kuo, "Numerical Methods and Computers." Addison-Wesley, Reading, Massachusetts, 1965. Although the error formulation in Kuo is somewhat different from the discussion here, the estimates of the truncation error by Eq. (4.21) above and Eq. (13.18) in Kuo are equivalent.

Substituting this and Eq. (4.28) into Eq. (4.21),

$$E_{m+1} = E_m + \tau(-E_m) + e_{m+1}$$

$$= (1 - \tau)E_m + y_0 \frac{\tau^2}{2} (1 - \tau)^m \tag{4.29}$$

and

$$E_m = (1 - \tau)E_{m-1} + y_0 \frac{\tau^2}{2} (1 - \tau)^{m-1}$$

$$= my_0 \left(\frac{\tau^2}{2}\right) \frac{(1 - \tau)^m}{(1 - \tau)} \tag{4.30}$$

Let the interval $A = m\tau = 1$; then

$$E_m = y_0 \left(\frac{\tau}{2}\right) \frac{(1 - \tau)^{1/\tau}}{(1 - \tau)} \tag{4.31}$$

For small τ,

$$\frac{1}{1 - \tau} \approx 1 \qquad \text{and} \qquad (1 - \tau)^{1/\tau} \approx e^{-1}$$

Thus Eq. (4.31) becomes

$$E_m = y_0 \frac{\tau}{2} e^{-1}$$

Since we choose $\tau = 0.001$ and were given $y_0 = 1$, we have

$$E_m = \frac{1 \times 0.001 e^{-1}}{2} = 0.00018394$$

The actual error as determined by subtracting the solution by Eq. (4.15) from the analytic solution e^{-1} is

$$0.36787946 - 0.36769549 = 0.00018397$$

which compares remarkably well with the theoretical error E_m. The results of this example with $\tau = 0.001$ and $\tau = 0.0001$ are summarized in Table 4.4.

As expected, the error decreases for the smaller increment size. However, the error estimate is less accurate because the round-off error increases with the smaller increment size, and this error estimate (Eq. 4.21) considers only the truncation error.

TABLE 4.4

TRUNCATION ERRORS

1	Interval	$\tau = 0.001$	$\tau = 0.0001$
2	e^{-1}	0.36787946	0.36787946
3	Approximate solution	0.36769549	0.36786087
4	Actual error (2–3)	0.00018397	0.00001859
5	Theoretical error (E_m)	0.00018394	0.00001839
6	Accuracy of error estimate (5–6)	0.00000003	0.00000020

In the next section we shall discuss the optimum selection of the increment size to minimize the net effects of both round-off errors and truncation errors.

EXAMPLE 4.4

Consider the differential equation

$$T_s \frac{dx}{dt} + x(t) = k(t)$$

$$Ts(x) * [1, -1] + s(x) = s(K)$$

where $T = T_s/\tau$,

$$s(x) = \frac{s(K)}{T[1, -1] + [1]}$$

For $k(t) = u(t)$,

$$s(x) = \frac{[1, 1, 1, \ldots]}{[T + 1, -T]}$$

$$= [1, 1, 1, \ldots] - \frac{[T]}{[T + 1, -T]}$$

$$= \left[1 - \frac{T}{T + 1}, 1 - \left(\frac{T}{T + 1}\right)^2, 1 - \left(\frac{T}{T + 1}\right)^3, \ldots\right]$$

In general,

$$x_n = 1 - \left(\frac{T}{T + 1}\right)^n = 1 - \left(1 + \frac{\tau}{T_s}\right)^{-n}$$

For $n = t/\tau$,

$$x(t) = x(n\tau) = x_n = 1 - \left(1 + \frac{\tau}{T_s}\right)^{-t/\tau}$$

and

$$\lim_{\tau \to 0} x(t) = \lim_{\tau \to 0} \left[1 - \left(1 + \frac{\tau}{T_s}\right)^{-t/\tau}\right] = 1 - e^{-t/T_s}$$

which is the exact solution.

For this example we can determine the exact error:

$$E_n = 1 - e^{-nt/T_s} - 1 + \left(1 + \frac{\tau}{T_s}\right)^{-n}$$

For $\tau/T_s = x < 1$,

$$E_n = \frac{1}{(1 + x)^n} - e^{-nx}$$

$$= 1 - nx + \frac{n(n-1)x^2}{2!} - \frac{n(n-1)(n-2)x^3}{3!} - \cdots - 1$$

$$+ nx - \frac{(nx)^2}{2!} + \frac{(nx)^3}{3!} - \cdots$$

$$= - \frac{nx^2}{2!} + (3n^2 - 2n)\frac{x^3}{6} + \cdots$$

$$\approx - \frac{nx^2}{2}$$

4.4 SELECTING THE INDEPENDENT VARIABLE INCREMENT

The accuracy of a calculation depends upon the truncation errors and the round-off errors. To keep the truncation error small, we choose τ small. On the other hand, more steps must be performed for small τ, thus increasing the round-off errors. Consistent with obtaining required accuracy, it is desirable to maintain τ as large as possible in order to minimize the computational effort. If the round-off error is the limiting factor, τ should be adjusted so that the truncation error and the round-off error are comparable. The existence of such an ideal increment size below which the total error increases does show that there is danger in choosing τ too small.

4.4.1 Optimum Increment Selection†

A desirable increment selection would effect a trade-off between the errors and computational effort. The inclusion of the computational effort into an error formulation allows this optimum increment selection. The error in the frequency domain (from Sec. 4.2) is

$$E(j\omega) = y(j\omega) - y_A(j\omega) \tag{4.32}$$

where $y(j\omega)$ is the ideal system response and $y_A(j\omega)$ is the approximate response.

Let $T_A(j\omega)$ represent the transfer function of the discrete approximation to the system $T(j\omega)$ having input $X(j\omega)$ and output $Y_A(j\omega)$. Then

$$E(j\omega) = \frac{1}{\tau} \sum_{n=-\infty}^{\infty} T\left[j\left(\omega - \frac{2n\pi}{\tau}\right)\right] X\left[j\left(\omega - \frac{2n\pi}{\tau}\right)\right]$$

$$- \frac{1}{\tau^2} \sum_{n=-\infty}^{\infty} T_A\left[j\left(\omega - \frac{2n\pi}{\tau}\right)\right] \sum_{m=-\infty}^{\infty} X\left[j\left(\omega - \frac{2m\pi}{\tau}\right)\right] \tag{4.33}$$

where the first term on the right is the sampled output of the ideal system and the second term is the output of the discrete approximation with sampled input and output. (See Tou [41].)

The power spectrum of the error is defined as

$$S(\omega) = E(j\omega)E(-j\omega) = |E(j\omega)|^2 \tag{4.34}$$

and the squared error is

$$E^2(t) = \sum_{n=0}^{\infty} [y(n\tau) - Y_A(n\tau)]^2 = \sum_{n=0}^{\infty} e_n{}^2$$

$$= \frac{1}{2\pi} \int_{-\infty}^{\infty} S(\omega)\, d\omega \tag{4.35}$$

(See Papoulis [27].)

Equation (4.35) may be evaluated as a function of the independent variable increment τ to obtain the maximum τ consistent with the required accuracy requirements. It is convenient, and probably more meaningful, to weight the error given in Eq. (4.35) by the increment size so that over a fixed interval,

---

† This section follows the development of Rosko and Durling [38] and Rosko [37].

identical functions yield the same mean square error, since Eq. (4.35) increases with the number of samples. Thus we define the mean squared error to be

$$\overline{E^2(t)} = \tau \sum_{n=0}^{\infty} e_n^{\,2} = \frac{\tau}{2\pi} \int_{-\infty}^{\infty} S(\omega)\, d\omega \qquad (4.36)$$

This procedure will be demonstrated in the next example.

EXAMPLE 4.5

Using the Tustin [45] substitution for the transfer function,

$$H(s) = \frac{s^2 + 17.25s + 4.25}{s^4 + 3s^3 + 7.25s^2 + 9.5s + 4.25}$$

τ was varied to obtain $E^2(t) = 0.10 \pm 0.0075$ in the simulated step response via a Newton-Raphson search, yielding the results shown in Table 4.5. The resultant step response for $\tau = 0.1634431$ is given in Problem 4.6 (Appendix).

TABLE 4.5

EXAMPLE 4.5, OPTIMUM TIME INCREMENT

Time increment		Mean square error	
τ_1	1.0	E_1	0.7689 6089
τ_2	0.1300 4562	E_2	0.0203 2629
τ_3	0.5855 4041	E_3	0.2569 2108
τ_4	0.4752 0608	E_4	0.1781 6538
τ_5	0.3925 7261	E_5	0.1302 3455
$\tau = \tau_6$	0.3460 6721	$\overline{E^2(t)} = E_6$	0.1063 4431

In general it is desirable to obtain a trade-off between the error and the computation time. The present problem is to minimize some criterion function of the error and the computation time:

$$J = f(\overline{E^2(t)}, \tau, \ldots) \qquad (4.37)$$

For example, if the computation time varies inversely with τ, Eq. 4.37 may be written

$$J = \overline{E^2(t)} + \mu \frac{1}{\tau} \qquad (4.38)$$

where μ is the cost factor weighting the computation time in relation to the error. Since $\overline{E^2(t)}$ is large for large τ and approaches zero for small τ (neglecting round-off errors), it is clear that Eq. (4.38) has a minimum in the interval $0 < \tau < \infty$. This minimization is shown in the next example.

EXAMPLE 4.6

Using the Tustin [45] substitution, and the system and excitation of Example 4.5, it is desired to minimize the functional (Eq. 4.39) by successive approximation:

$$J = \overline{E^2(t)} + 0.1\frac{1}{\tau} \tag{4.39}$$

It is assumed that J has been minimized when the relative change in successive values of τ and J are less than 0.001 and 0.05, respectively. The resultant increments and functional values are given in Table 4.6.

TABLE 4.6

EXAMPLE 4.6, OPTIMUM τ

Time increment		Performance index	
τ_1	1.0	J_1	0.8689 6089
τ_2	0.3606 1839	J_2	0.3909 1140
$\tau = \tau_3$	0.3995 6613	$J_{opt} = J_3$	0.3842 7159

Table 4.7 gives the optimum increment selection for this example for several of the substitutional operators.

TABLE 4.7

COMPARISON OF THE PERFORMANCE INDEX AND ITS COMPONENTS FOR EACH TECHNIQUE AS APPLIED TO EXAMPLE 4.6

Method	Performance index, J	Erorr, $\overline{E^2(t)}$	Time increment, τ
Tustin [45]	0.38427159	0.13400013	0.39956613
Madwed [23]	0.45199638	0.15126943	0.33252756
Boxer-Thaler [4]	0.49315241	0.15686261	0.29736257
First difference	0.84110796	0.41978290	0.23734643
z-transform	0.75016771	0.22642158	0.19093220
Halijak [16]	0.74355045	0.22988748	0.19468018

4.4.2   Variable Increment Schemes

If a formula exists for the error per step, it is possible to devise a variable increment technique. The usual procedure is to change τ such that the error per step is less than some specified maximum. If the error is less than the predetermined error E, τ is doubled; and if it is greater than E, τ is halved. The effect is to reduce τ when the solution or response is rapidly varying and to enlarge τ when the solution is essentially constant. These schemes are suitable primarily for single-step schemes where the recursion relation contains only the present and immediate past values of excitation and response. For these single-step schemes, the sample interval may be varied to maintain the rate of error accumulation below an upper bound [12].

In the case of the first difference, or Euler integration,

$$y(T) = \int_a^T f(t) \, dt \approx \sum_{n=0}^{N-1} f_n \tau_n \tag{4.40}$$

where

$$\sum_{n=0}^{N-1} \tau_n = T - a \qquad \text{and} \qquad f_n = \begin{cases} f(0), & n = 0 \\ f\left[\sum_{i=0}^{n-1} \tau_i\right], & n > 0 \end{cases}$$

the error in each interval τ_n is

$$e_n = \frac{\tau_n{}^2}{2} f'(t_x)$$

where t_x is in the interval τ_i and

$$e_n \approx \frac{\tau_n{}^2}{2} \frac{f_{n+1} - f_n}{\tau_n} = \frac{\tau_n}{2} (f_{n+1} - f_n) \tag{4.41}$$

for

$$I_n = y_{n+1} - y_n = f_n \tau_n$$

For trapezoidal integration we have

$$I_n = \frac{\tau_n}{2} (f_n + f_{n+1})$$

and

$$e_n = \frac{-\tau_n{}^3}{12} f''(\tau_n)$$

$$\approx \frac{-\tau_n{}^3}{12} \left[\left(\frac{2}{\tau_n + \tau_{n-1}}\right) \left(\frac{f_{n+1} - f_n}{\tau_n} - \frac{f_n - f_{n-1}}{\tau_{n-1}}\right) \right] \tag{4.42}$$

If it is desired to limit the rate of error accumulation to a maximum of A per unit of t, we have, by Eq. (4.41), the error accumulation in the nth interval:

$$\left|\frac{e_n}{\tau_n}\right| \approx \left|\frac{f_{n+1} - f_n}{2}\right| < A \tag{4.43}$$

Then it is necessary to require that $|e_n/\tau_n| < A$, which can always be satisfied if $f(t)$ is continuous. The total error resulting from the integration is less than $A(T - a)$, since

$$\left|\sum_{n=0}^{N-1} e_n\right| = \left|\sum_{n=0}^{N-1} \tau_n \frac{[f_{n+1} - f_n]}{2}\right|$$

$$\leq \sum_{n=0}^{N-1} \tau_n \left|\frac{f_{n+1} - f_n}{2}\right| < A \sum_{n=0}^{N-1} \tau_n = A(T - a) \tag{4.44}$$

For trapezoidal integration we need only require, by Eq. (4.42), that

$$\left|\frac{e_n}{n}\right| = \frac{\tau_n}{6\tau_{n-1}(\tau_n + \tau_{n-1})} \cdot \left|\tau_{n-1}(f_{n+1} - f_n) - \tau_n(f_n - f_{n-1})\right| < A \tag{4.45}$$

and for $n = 0$, we may choose $f_{n-1} = f_n$ while τ_{-1} is arbitrary.

TABLE 4.8

$$\int_0^{10} e^{-x}\, dx, \; A = 0.01$$

x	e^{-x}	$\int_0^{10} e^{-x}\, dx$
0.	1.00000	0.
0.12500	0.88249	0.11765
0.37500	0.68728	0.31387
0.62500	0.53526	0.46669
0.87500	0.41686	0.58571
1.37500	0.25283	0.75313
1.87500	0.15335	0.85468
2.37500	0.09301	0.91628
3.37500	0.03421	0.97989
5.37500	0.00463	1.01874
7.37500	0.00008	1.02817
10.00000	0.00004	1.02821

EXAMPLE 4.7

The procedure given above was carried out for the integral

$$I = \int_0^{10} e^{-x} \, dx = 1 - e^{-10} \approx 0.99995$$

using the trapezoidal rule and Eq. (4.45). We obtain, with $A = 0.01$, the ordinates and values presented in Table 4.8.

Trapezoidal integration with 11 equally spaced intervals yields the value $I = 1.06789$.

For this example the increment was either halved, held constant, or doubled at each step. Thus Eq. (4.45) was calculated at most twice for each increment. Of course changing the increment to make $|e_n/\tau_n| \approx A$ would require slightly more computation time.

CHAPTER 5 Applications of Impulse Analysis to Control Problems

INTRODUCTION

The applications of impulse analysis are very broad. This discrete-time approach can be taken into consideration for the analysis of various systems, especially when the analytical formulation of the relationships among the system parameters are unknown and when the relationships are to be determined from measured input and output data.

This last chapter deals with some applications of impulse analysis to control problems. The first two sections describe the use of impulse analysis to determine the system response to deterministic and stochastic inputs. The last three sections are related to the analysis of multivariable systems, system identification, and nonlinear control systems.

5.1 SYSTEM RESPONSE TO DETERMINISTIC INPUTS

5.1.1 Responses to Isolated Disturbances

For the closed loop system shown in Fig. 5.1,

$$C(t) = \text{controlled variable (output)}$$

$$k(t) = \text{load variable (input or disturbance)}$$

$$R(s) = \text{controller transfer function}$$

$$P(s) = \text{plant transfer function (process)}$$

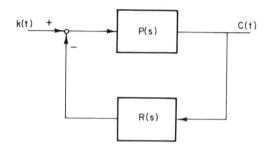

FIG. 5.1   Isolated disturbance applied to feedback system.

The input-output transfer relation is

$$C(s) = \frac{P(s)}{1 + P(s)R(s)} K(s)$$

where

$$C(s) = \text{the Laplace transform of } C(t)$$
$$K(s) = \text{the Laplace transform of } k(t)$$

Let

$$g_k(t) = \mathcal{L}^{-1}[P(s)]$$
$$g_r(t) = \mathcal{L}^{-1}[P(s)R(s)]$$

Then, if

$$g_k(t) = g_r(t) = k(t) = C(t) = 0 \qquad \text{for} \qquad t < 0$$

$$C(t) = \int_0^t g_k(t - \theta)k(\theta) \, d\theta - \int_0^t g_r(t - \theta)C(\theta) \, d\theta$$

In physical systems the response characteristics are usually given by experimental data. If $k(t)$, $g_k(t)$, and $g_r(t)$ are known, possibly as experimental data, at a sequence of points these convolution integrals can be evaluated by the procedures of Sec. 2.2. Thus

$$S(C) = \tau S(k) * S(g_k) - \tau S(C) * S(g_r)$$

and with the intermediate value sequence,

$$S(C) = \tau[S_i(k) * S_i(g_k)]D(-1) - \tau[S(C) * S_i(g_r)]$$

or

$$S(C) = \frac{\tau[S_i(k) * S_i(g_k)]D(-1)}{[1] + \tau S_i(g_r)} \qquad (5.1)$$

$C(t)$ may also be obtained by taking

$$C(t) = \int_0^t \gamma_k(t - \theta)k(\theta)\, d\theta - \int_0^t \dot{\gamma}_r(t - \theta)C(\theta)\, d\theta$$

where

$$k(t) = \frac{dk}{dt}$$

(see Sec. 2.2.3)

$$\dot{\gamma}_r(t) = g_r(t) \qquad \text{and} \qquad \gamma_k(t) = \int_0^t g_k(t)\, dt$$

$\gamma_r(t)$ and $\gamma_k(t)$ are the step responses of $P(s)R(s)$, and $P(s)$, respectively. Thus we have

$$S(C) = \tau S(\gamma_k) * S(\dot{k}) - \tau S(\dot{\gamma}_r) * S(C)$$
$$= \frac{\tau S(\gamma_k) * S(\dot{k})}{[1] + \tau S(\dot{\gamma}_r)}$$

Using the central difference and neglecting the correction term,

$$S(C) = \frac{S(\gamma_k) * S_i(k) * [1, -1]}{[1] + S_i(\gamma_r) * [1, -1]}$$
$$= \frac{S_i(k) * S(\gamma_k)}{[1, 1, 1, \ldots] + S_i(\gamma_r)} \tag{5.2}$$

The equation

$$S(C) = \tau S(k) * S(g_k) - \tau S(C) * S(g_r)$$

may be integrated by the trapezoidal rule convolution to obtain for the nth term of $S(C)$:

$$C_n = \tau\left(\frac{g_{k_0}k_n}{2} + g_{k_1}k_{n-1} + \cdots + g_{k_{n-1}}k_1 + \frac{g_{k_n}k_0}{2}\right)$$
$$- \tau\left(\frac{g_{r_0}C_n}{2} + g_{r_1}C_{n-1} + \cdots + \frac{g_{r_n}C_0}{2}\right)$$
$$= \frac{\tau}{1 + (\tau/2)g_0}\left[\left(\frac{g_{k_0}k_n}{2} + g_{k_1}k_{n-1} + \cdots + \frac{g_{k_n}k_0}{2}\right)\right.$$
$$\left. - \left(g_{r_1}C_{n-1} + \cdots + g_{r_{n-1}}C_1 + \frac{g_{r_n}C_0}{2}\right)\right]$$
$$= \frac{1}{1 + (\tau/2)g_0}(C_{kn} - \Sigma_n)$$

where

$$C_{k_n} = \tau\left(\frac{g_{k_0}k_n}{2} + g_{k_1}k_{n-1} + \cdots + g_{k_{n-1}}k_1 + \frac{g_{k_n}k_0}{2}\right)$$

or

$$S(C_k) = \tau S(G) * S(k)$$

and

$$\Sigma_n = \tau\left(\frac{g_{rn}C_0}{2} + g_{r_{n-1}}C_1 + \cdots + g_{r_1}C_{n-1}\right)$$

which may be carried out by the following tabular algorithm:

n	C_{k_n}	$C_{k_n} - \Sigma_n$	C_n	τg_{r1}	τg_{r2}	τg_{r3}	τg_{r4}
0	C_{k_0}	C_{k_0}	$C_0 = \dfrac{C_{k_0}}{1 + (\tau/2)g_0}$	$\tau g_{r1}\dfrac{C_0}{2}$	$\tau g_{r2}\dfrac{C_0}{2}$	$\tau g_{r3}\dfrac{C_0}{2}$	$\cdots$
1	C_{k_1}	$C_{k_1} - \Sigma_1$	$C_1 = \dfrac{C_{k_1} - \Sigma_1}{1 + (\tau/2)g_0}$	Σ_1	$\tau g_{r1}C_1$	$\tau g_{r2}C_1$	$\cdots$
2	C_{k_2}	$C_{k_2} - \Sigma_2$	$C_2 = \dfrac{C_{k_2} - \Sigma_2}{1 + (\tau/2)g_0}$		Σ_2	$\tau g_{r1}C_2$	$\cdots$
3	C_{k_3}	$C_{k_3} - \Sigma_3$	$C_3 =$			Σ_3	$\cdots$
4	C_{k_4}	$\vdots$	$\vdots$	$\vdots$			

EXAMPLE 5.1

Consider the system shown in Fig. 5.2.

$$P(s) = P(s)R(s) = \frac{1}{sT}$$

$$\gamma_k(t) = \gamma_r(t) = \frac{t}{T}u(t)$$

$$g_k(t) = g_r(t) = \frac{1}{T}u(t)$$

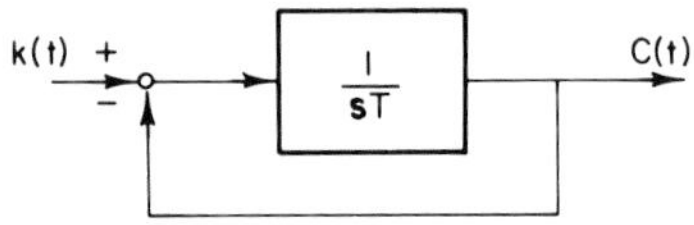

FIG. 5.2 Example 5.1.

Taking $T = 5$ and $\tau = 1$, we have

$$S(\gamma_k) = S(\gamma_r) = 0.2[0, 1, 2, 3, 4, \ldots]$$
$$S_i(\gamma_k) = S_i(\gamma_r) = [0.3, 0.1, 0.5, 0.7, \ldots]$$
$$S(g_k) = S(g_r) = 0.2[0.5, 1, 1, 1, \ldots]$$
$$S_i(g_k) = S_i(g_r) = 0.2[1, 1, 1, 1, \ldots]$$

Using the impulse response to determine the system response to $k(t) = u(t)$,

$$S_1(C) = \frac{[1, 1, 1, 1, \ldots] * [1, 1, 1, \ldots]D(-1)}{[1] + [0.2, 0.2, 0.2, \ldots]}$$
$$= [0, 0.182, 0.329, 0.451, 0.551, 0.632, \ldots]$$

With the step response,

$$S_2(C) = \frac{[1, 1, 1, \ldots] * [0, 0.2, 0.4, 0.6, \ldots]}{[1, 1, 1, \ldots] + [0.1, 0.3, 0.5, 0.7, \ldots]}$$
$$= [0, 0.182, 0.329, 0.452, 0.551, 0.632, \ldots]$$

and with the recursion table, using the trapezoidal rule, we have

$$\frac{1}{1 + (\tau/2)g_0} = \frac{1}{1.1} \doteq 0.909$$

n	C_{kn}	$C_{kn} - \Sigma_n$	$C_n = s_3(C)$	0.2	0.2	0.2	0.2	0.2	$\cdots$
0	0	0	0	0	0	0	0	0	$\cdots$
1	0.2	0.2	0.182	0	0.0364	0.0364	0.0364	0.0364	$\cdots$
2	0.4	0.3636	0.331		0.0364	0.0662	0.0662	0.0662	$\cdots$
3	0.6	0.4874	0.452			0.1026	0.0904	0.0904	$\cdots$
4	0.8	0.6070	0.551				0.1903	0.1104	$\cdots$
5	1.0	0.6966	0.633					0.3034	
$\vdots$	$\vdots$	$\vdots$	$\vdots$						

The results are presented in Table 5.1 for comparison with the exact sequence.

EXAMPLE 5.2

Consider the system shown in Fig. 5.3.

Determine the step response when

$$T_r = 10, \qquad T = 2, \qquad T_i = 0, 2 \quad \text{(seconds)}$$

TABLE 5.1

EXAMPLE 5.1

Exact	$S_1(C)$	$S_2(C)$	$S_3(C)$
0	0	0	0
0.1813	0.182	0.182	0.182
0.3298	0.329	0.329	0.331
0.4512	0.451	0.452	0.452
0.5507	0.551	0.551	0.551
0.6321	0.632	0.632	0.633
0.6988	0.699	0.699	0.700

For $T_i = 0$,

$$\gamma_k(t) = (1 - e^{-(t/2)})u(t), \qquad \gamma_r(t) = \tfrac{1}{10}(t + 2e^{-(t/2)})u(t)$$
$$g_k(t) = \tfrac{1}{2}e^{-(t/2)}u(t), \qquad g_r(t) = \tfrac{1}{10}(1 - e^{-(t/2)})u(t)$$

For $\tau = 1$,

$$S(g_k) = [0.5, 0.303, 0.184, 0.111, 0.067, 0.041, 0.025,$$
$$0.015, 0.009, 0.006, 0.004, \dots]$$

$$S(\gamma_k) = [0, 0.3937, 0.6320, 0.7770, 0.8645, 0.9180, 0.9511,$$
$$0.9698, 0.9813, 0.9890, 0.9930, \dots]$$

$$S(g_r) = [0, 0.0394, 0.0632, 0.0777, 0.0865, 0.0918, 0.0951,$$
$$0.0970, 0.0982, 0.0989, 0.0993, \dots]$$

$$S_i(g_r) = [0.0198, 0.0513, 0.0705, 0.0822, 0.0893, 0.0935,$$
$$0.0961, 0.0976, 0.0986, 0.0991, \dots]$$

$$S(\gamma_r) = [0, 0.0210, 0.0736, 0.1444, 0.2268, 0.3162, 0.4098,$$
$$0.5060, 0.6036, 0.7022, 0.8014, \dots]$$

$$S_i(\gamma_r) = [0.011, 0.0473, 0.1090, 0.1860, 0.272, 0.363,$$
$$0.458, 0.555, 0.633, 0.752, \dots]$$

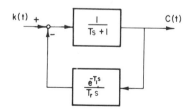

FIG. 5.3   Example 5.2.

Thus

$$S_o(C) = \frac{S_i(k) * S(\gamma_k)}{[1, 1, 1, \ldots] + S_i(\gamma_r)}$$

$$= [0, 0.391, 0.611, 0.724, 0.761, 0.757, 0.727, 0.676, 0.616,$$
$$0.558, 0.496, \ldots]$$

which compares favorably with the exact solution

$$C(t) = 2.24(e^{-0.1382t} - e^{-0.3618t})$$

$$S(C) = [0, 0.390, 0.611, 0.721, 0.760, 0.754, 0.720, 0.672, 0.616, 0.588, \ldots]$$

using the trapezoidal rule we obtain the results

$$S_T(C) = [0, 0.3937, 0.6165, 0.7278, 0.7663, 0.7598, 0.7257,$$
$$0.6757, 0.6204, \ldots]$$

which obviously is not as accurate as the deconvolution solution.

With $T_i = 2$, we have

$$S_i(\gamma_r) = [0, 0, 0, 0.011, 0.0473, 0.1090, 0.186, 0.272, 0.363,$$
$$0.458, 0.555, 0.633, 0.752, \ldots]$$

and

$$S_2(C) = [0, 0.395, 0.632, 0.773, 0.844, 0.866, 0.842, 0.842,$$
$$0.799, 0.741, 0.670, 0.605, \ldots]$$

Using the trapezoidal rule, we have

$$S_{T_2}(C) = [0, 0.394, 0.632, 0.777, 0.849, 0.868, 0.849, 0.804, 0.738, \ldots]$$

EXAMPLE 5.3

Consider the control system shown in Fig. 5.4.
The transfer function of the system is

$$H(s) = \frac{e^{-sT_i}/s}{1 + (e^{-sT_i}/s)}$$

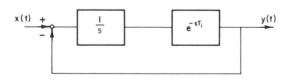

FIG. 5.4   Example 5.3, feedback system.

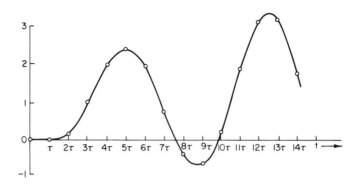

FIG. **5.5**   Example 5.3, step response.

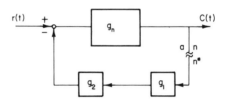

FIG. **5.6**   Closed-loop stability.

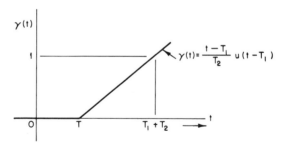

FIG. **5.7**   Systems stability from the open-loop step response characterized by a delayed ramp. Conditions are: 1. Closed loop stable for $T_1/T_2 \leq \pi/2$. 2. Natural frequency, $\omega_0 = (\pi/2)(1/T_1)$. 3. Critical damping, $T_1/T_2 = 1/e$. 4. Time constant for critical damping, $T_0 = T_1$.

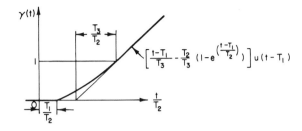

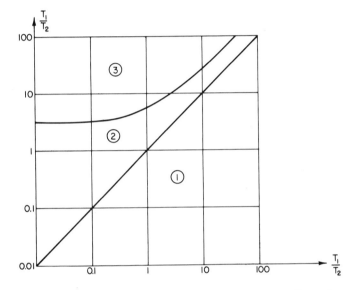

FIG. **5.8** System stability from the open-loop step response. Curve 1: unstable; curve 2, stable, periodic; curve 3, stable, aperiodic.

For $x(t) = u(t)$,

$$Y(s) = \frac{e^{-sT_i}/s^2}{1 + (e^{-sT_i}/s)}$$

Using the Naslin [25] substitution, we have (for $n =$ the nearest integer to τ_i/τ)

$$Y(z) = \frac{z^{-n}\left(\dfrac{T^2}{8}\dfrac{z^2 + 6z + 1}{(z-1)^2}\right)}{1 + z^{-n}\left(\dfrac{T}{2}\left(\dfrac{z+1}{z-1}\right)\right)}$$

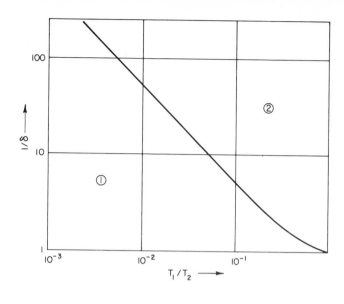

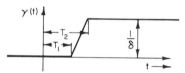

FIG. **5.9** System stability from the open-loop step response. Area 1, stable; area 2, unstable.

or

$$Y(z) = \frac{T^2}{4} \frac{z^{-n}(z^2 + 6z + 1)}{(z - 1)(Tz^{-n+1} + Tz^{-n} + 2z - 2)}$$

for $T = 2$ and $\tau = 1$,

$$Y(z) = \frac{1}{4} \frac{1 + 6z^{-1} + z^{-2}}{2z^2 - 4z + 3 - z^{-2}} = \frac{1}{4} \frac{z^{-2} + 6z^{-3} + z^{-1}}{2 - 4z^{-1} + 3z^{-2} - z^{-4}}$$

or

$$S(Y) = \frac{1}{4} \frac{[0, 0, 1, 6, 1]}{[2, -4, 3, 0, -1]}$$

$$= [0, 0, 0.125, 1.0, 1.938, 2.375, 1.906, 0.750, -0.391, -0.656,$$
$$0.227, 1.183, 3.090, 3.133, 1.744, \ldots]$$

Figure 5.5 is a plot of the system step response.

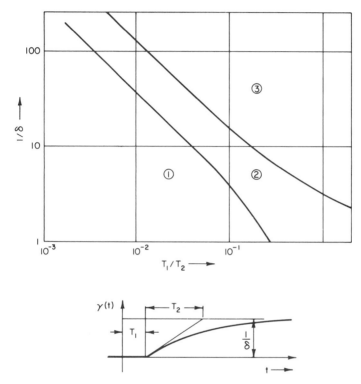

FIG. **5.10** System stability from the open-loop step response. Area 1, unstable-nonperiodic; area 2, stable-periodic; area 3, unstable.

5.1.2 Stability Conditions of Control Systems

If the transfer characteristics (frequency response) of each element of a feedback control system are known, the stability of the closed-loop system may be investigated by any of the well-known stability criteria. Thus system stability may be investigated with the aid of the system identification techniques presented in Chapter 5.

This chapter presents the stability conditions for some sample step responses. If the computed step response of the system can be approximated by one of those presented, an indication of closed-loop stability and performance is obtained.

Consider the closed-loop system shown in Fig. 5.6.

The loop is opened at some convenient point (*a* in Fig. 5.6, an arbitrary

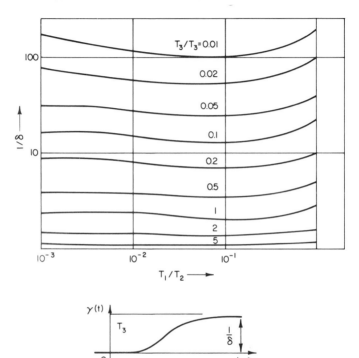

FIG. **5.11**   System stability from the open-loop step response.

$$\gamma(t) = \frac{1}{\delta}\left[1 + \frac{1}{T_1 - T_2}[(T_2 e^{-(t-T_3)/T_2}) - (T_1 e^{-(t-T_3)/T_1})]u(t - T_3)\right].$$

signal is injected into $n^*(t)$ and the response $n(t)$ is measured. The loop step response $S(\gamma)$ is then

$$S(\gamma) = \frac{S(n)}{S(n^*)} * [1, 1, 1, \ldots]$$

Of course if $n^*(t)$ is a step, $S(\gamma) = S(n)$. For a type 0 system, $\gamma(t)$ becomes asymptotically constant for large t. For a type 1 system, $\gamma(t)$ becomes asymptotically linear for large t.

Figures 5.7 through 5.11 give several system step responses of type 0 and type 1 systems with delay elements and their associated regions of stability.†

---

† From S. R. C. Oldenburg and H. Sartorius, "Dynamik selbstätiger Regelungen." Oldenburg Verlag, München and Berlin, 1951.

5.2 SYSTEM RESPONSE TO STOCHASTIC INPUTS

A linear system with random input $x(t)$ and output $y(t)$ is shown in Fig. 5.12.

Definitions:

1. Mean value of a random variable $x(t)$:

$$\bar{x} = \lim_{T \to \infty} \frac{1}{2T} \int_{-T}^{T} x(t)\, dt$$

2. Variance of a random variable $x(t)$:

$$\sigma_x{}^2 = \lim_{T \to \infty} \frac{1}{2T} \int_{-T}^{T} (x - \bar{x})^2\, dt$$

3. Autocorrelation function (for stationary $x(t)$):

$$R_{xx}(\theta) = \lim_{T \to \infty} \frac{1}{2T} \int_{-T}^{T} x(t)x(t + \theta)\, dt$$

4. Cross-correlation function between $x(t)$ and $y(t)$:

$$R_{xy}(\theta) = \lim_{T \to \infty} \frac{1}{2T} \int_{-T}^{T} x(t)y(t + \theta)\, dt$$

($R_{xx}(\theta)$ is an even function of θ.)

Frequently in physical systems the random variables may be assumed to have a Gaussian probability density:

$$p(x) = \frac{1}{2\pi\sigma} \exp\left(-\frac{x - \bar{x}}{2\sigma^2}\right)$$

We may *define* the spectral density ϕ_{xx} of a function $x(t)$ to be the Fourier transform of the autocorrelation function

$$\phi_{xx}(\omega) = \int_{-\infty}^{\infty} R_{xx}(\theta)e^{-j\omega\theta}\, d\theta$$

$$= 2 \int_{0}^{\infty} R_{xx}(\theta) \cos \omega\theta\, d\theta$$

and the inverse transform yields

$$R_{xx}(\theta) = \frac{1}{2\pi} \int_{-\infty}^{\infty} \phi_{xx}(\omega)e^{j\omega\theta}\, d\omega = \frac{1}{\pi} \int_{0}^{\infty} \phi_{xx}(\omega) \cos \omega\theta\, d\omega$$

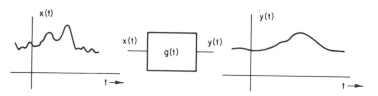

FIG. **5.12**   Transfer element with random input.

provided $\int_{-\infty}^{\infty} |R_{xx}(\theta)|\, d\theta < \infty$, which is usually satisfied. It is easy to show that

$$R_{xx}(0) = \lim_{T \to \infty} \frac{1}{2T} \int_{-\infty}^{\infty} x^2(t)\, dt = \overline{x^2}$$

$$= \frac{1}{2\pi} \int_{-\infty}^{\infty} \phi_{xx}(\omega)\, d\omega$$

The input and output autocorrelation functions are related to the impulse response of the system by the double convolution integral

$$R_{yy}(\theta) = \iint_{-\infty}^{\infty} g(\alpha)g(\beta)R_{xx}(\theta + \alpha - \beta)\, d\alpha\, d\beta$$

The cross-correlation function is given by

$$R_{xy}(\theta) = \int_{0}^{\infty} g(\alpha)R_{xx}(\theta - \alpha)\, d\alpha$$

which has been evaluated in Sec. 2.2.1.

Considering the double convolution,

$$R_{yy}(\theta) = \int_{-\infty}^{\infty} R_{xx}(\theta - \beta) \int_{0}^{\infty} g(\alpha)g(\alpha + \beta)\, d\alpha\, d\beta$$

$$g(\alpha) = 0 \qquad \text{for } \alpha < 0$$

Defining the autocorrelation function of the impulse response,

$$R_g(u) = \int_{0}^{\infty} g(z)g(z + u)\, dz$$

(Note that $R_g(u)$ is an even function.)

We have

$$R_{yy}(\theta) = \int_{0}^{\infty} R_{xx}(u - \theta)R_g(u)\, du + \int_{0}^{\infty} R_{xx}(u + \theta)R_g(u)\, du \tag{5.3}$$

Figure 5.13(a) shows the integrand $R_{xx}(\theta + u)R_g(u)$ and its contribution

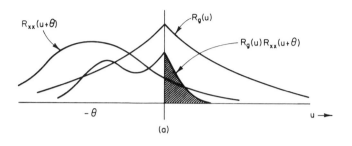

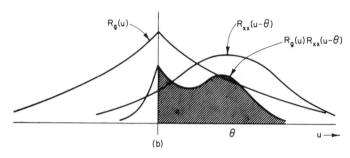

FIG. **5.13**   Computation of the autocorrelation of the output.

to $R_{yy}(\theta)$. Figure 5.13(b) shows the integrand $R_{xx}(\theta - u)R_g(u)$ and its contribution to $R_{yy}(\theta)$.
For $\theta = 0$, we have

$$R_{yy}(0) = \overline{x^2} = 2 \int_0^\infty R_{xx}(u)R_g(u)\,du$$

Letting

$$S(R_{xx}(\theta)) = [rx_0, rx_1, rx_2, \ldots]$$
$$S(R_{yy}(\theta)) = [ry_0, ry_1, ry_2, \ldots]$$
$$S(R_g(\theta)) = [rg_0, rg_1, rg_2, \ldots]$$

where

$$rx_k = R_{xx}(k\tau)$$
$$ry_k = R_{yy}(k\tau)$$
$$rg_k = R_g(k\tau)$$

by trapezoidal integration† we have

$$R_{yy}(0) = ry_0 = 2\tau\left[\frac{rg_0 rx_0}{2} + rg_1 rx_1 + rg_2 rx_2 + \cdots\right]$$

---

† Of course any integration technique may be used.

In general

$$R_{yy}(n\tau) = ry_n$$

$$= \tau\left[\frac{rg_0 rx_n}{2} + rg_1 rx_{n-1} + \cdots + rg_n rx_0 + rg_{n+1} rx_1 + \cdots\right]$$

$$+ \tau\left[\frac{rg_0 rx_n}{2} + rg_1 rx_{n+1} + rg_2 rx_{n+2} + \cdots\right]$$

$$rg_n = \tau[rg_0(rx_n) + rg_1(rx_{n-1} + rx_{n+1}) + rg_2(rx_{n-2} + rx_{n+2})$$
$$+ \cdots + rg_n(rx_0 + rx2_n) + rg_{n+1}(rx_1 + rx_{2n+1})$$
$$+ \cdots]$$

This tabulation may be carried out by hand by writing the sequence $S(R_{xx}(\theta))$ on a strip of paper and passing it below a strip containing the sequence $S(R_{xx}(\theta))$ extending in both directions from rx_0. The sums then appear as

rx_3	rx_2	rx_1	rx_0	rx_1	rx_2	rx_3	$\cdots$

$\cdots$	rx_{2n-1}	rx_{2n}	rx_{2n+1}	rx_{2n+2}	$\cdots$

$$S(R^*) = [rx_n, rx_{n-1} + rx_{n+1}, \cdots]$$
$$= [R_0{}^*, R_1{}^*, \ldots, R_n{}^*, \ldots]$$

Then

$$S(R_{yy}(\theta)) = \sum_{k=0} R_k{}^* rg_k$$

In practice the autocorrelation and cross-correlation functions may not be determined exactly, since there are no infinite records of the random variables. There are several methods to approximate the correlation functions (see Blackman and Tukey [3]). The most straightforward method (although not necessarily the most efficient) of obtaining an approximation to $R_{xx}(\theta)$ from a record of length T_0 is to take

$$R_{xx}(\theta) = \lim_{T \to \infty} \frac{1}{2T} \int_{-T}^{T} x(t)x(t + \theta)\, dt \approx \frac{1}{T_0 - \theta} \int_0^{T_0 - \theta} x(t)x(t + \theta)\, dt$$

which is evaluated by any of the methods presented in Sec. 2.4. Choosing an interval size τ such that $N = T_0/\tau$ is an integer, for $\theta = k\tau$ we have

$$rx_k = R_{xx}(k\tau) \approx \frac{1}{N - k + 1} \sum_{n=0}^{N-k} x_n x_{n+k}$$

Also for a finite (T_0) record of $x(t)$ and $y(t)$, we have

$$rxy_k = R_{xy}(k\tau) \approx \frac{1}{N - k + 1} \sum_{n=0}^{N-k} x_n y_{n+k}$$

and for the autocorrelation of the impulse response,

$$S(R_g) = [rg_0, rg_1, rg_2, \ldots]$$

$$rg_k = R_g(k\tau) = \int_0^\infty g(z)g(z + k\tau)\, dz$$

$$\approx \tau \sum_{n=0}^\infty g_n g_{n+k}$$

which may be truncated to any acceptable accuracy, say,

$$rg_k \approx \tau \sum_{n=0}^N g_n g_{n+k}$$

For $\theta = 0$, we have

$$\overline{x^2} = R_{xx}(0) \approx \frac{1}{N + 1} \sum_{n=0}^N x_n^2$$

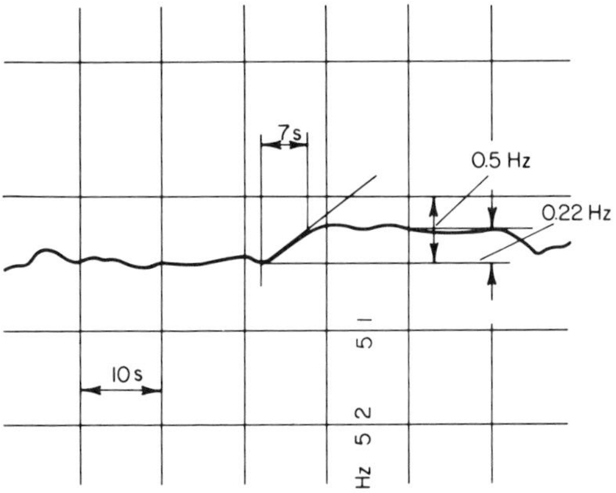

FIG. **5.14** Measured step response of a frequency control.

and

$$\overline{y^2} = R_{yy}(0) \approx \tau \left[rx_0 rg_0 + 2 \sum_{n=1}^{\infty} rx_n rg_n \right]$$

$$\approx \tau \left[rx_0 rg_0 + 2 \sum_{n=1}^{N} rx_n rg_n \right]$$

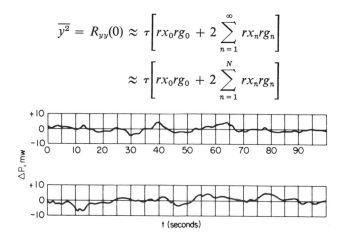

FIG. **5.15** Sample load variation of power system.

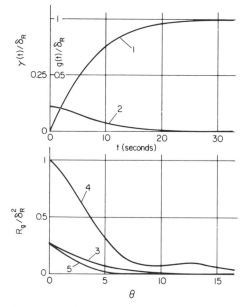

FIG. **5.16** Example determination of system response to stochastic inputs. Curve 1, unit response $\gamma(t)/\delta_R$; curve 2, impulse response $g(t)/\delta_R$; curve 3, autocorrelation function R_x/δ_R^2 for the impulse response $g(t)/\delta_R$; curve 4, autocorrelation function $R_x(\theta)/R_x(0)$ for load fluctuation; curve 5, product $R_g/\delta_R^2 \cdot R_x(\theta)/R_x(0)$.

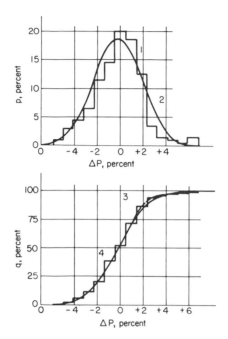

F<small>IG</small>. **5.17**   System response to stochastic excitation. Curve 1, measured distribution curve; curve 2, ideal Gaussian distribution curve for the same standard deviation.

E<small>XAMPLE</small> 5.4

Example 5.4 approximations computed above have been used to investigate the frequency control of a power distribution system. Figure 5.14 is a record of the measured step response of the system. The recording indicates the frequency change after a 73 MW step change in load. The step response is approximately exponential, with a time constant of 7 s. Figure 5.15 gives a sample of the load variations of the system. Figure 5.16(a) shows the step response and impulse responses taken from Fig. 5.14. The factor $1/\delta_R$ normalizes the step response to a fine value of 1. Figure 5.16(b) shows the approximate autocorrelation of the impulse response R_g (curve 3) taken from the record in Fig. 5.15. Curve 4 is the normalized autocorrelation function and curve 5 is the product of curves 3 and 4. Twice the integral of curve 5 is the mean square value of the random signal, which is approximately

$$\overline{y^2} \approx 0.335 \text{ percent}$$

This compares reasonably with the mean square value computed directly from the recorded samples that yielded values of 0.283 and 0.338 percent.

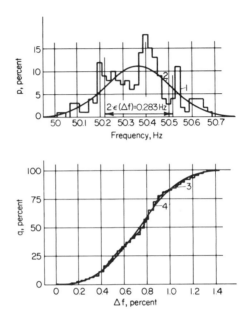

FIG. **5.18** System response to stochastic excitation. Curve 1, measured distribution curve; curve 2, ideal Gaussian distribution curve for the same standard deviation; curve 3, measured magnitude probability curve; curve 4, magnitude probability curve for ideal Gaussian distribution.

Figures 5.17 and 5.18 are the probability density and probability distribution of the samples shown in Fig. 5.15 and as compared with a Gaussian distribution.

5.3 MULTIVARIABLE SYSTEMS

5.3.1 Systems of Differential Equations

Systems of linear differential equations may be integrated by the procedures of Chapter 2. Consider the system of differential equations, with time-varying coefficients:

$$\dot{x}_1 = A_{11}(t)x_1 + A_{12}(t)x_2 + \cdots + A_{1n}(t)x_n + C_1(t)$$
$$\dot{x}_2 = A_{21}(t)x_1 + A_{22}(t)x_2 + \cdots + A_{2n}(t)x_n + C_2(t)$$
$$\vdots$$
$$\dot{x}_n = A_{n1}(t)x_1 + A_{n2}(t)x_2 + \cdots + A_{nn}(t)x_n + C_n(t)$$

It is assumed that the A_i, the C_k, and the initial conditions are known. Integrating once for the system, we have

$$x_i = \int_0^t A_{i1}(u)x_1(u)\ du + \cdots + \int_0^t A_{in}(u)x_n(u)\ du$$

$$+ \int_0^t C_i(u)\ du + x_i(0)$$

Using the matrix integrating operator, we have (35)

$$S(x_i) = \tau S(x_i)[\diagdown^{A_{i1}}][B] + \cdots$$
$$= \tau S(x_n)[\diagdown^{A_{in}}][B] + \tau S(C_i)[B]$$
$$+ x_i(0)[1, 1, 1, \ldots]$$

where $[\diagdown^{A_{ik}}]$ is the diagonal matrix with diagonal elements equal to the respective elements of $S(A_{ik})$ and $[B]$ is the integration matrix. This system may be written

$$S(x_1)[[1] - \tau[\diagdown^{A_{11}}][B]] + \cdots + \tau S(x_n)[\diagdown^{A_{in}}][B] = [Q_1]$$
$$\vdots$$
$$\tau S(x_1)[\diagdown^{A_{n1}}][B] + \cdots + S(x_n)[[1] - \tau[\diagdown^{A_{nn}}][B]] = [Q_n]$$

where

$$[Q_i] = x_i(0)[1, 1, 1, \ldots] + \tau[C_i][B]$$

which may be solved for the sequence $S(x_i)$.

Consider the case of two unknowns:

$$S(x_1)[P_{11}] + S(x_2)[P_{12}] = [Q_1]$$
$$S(x_1)[P_{21}] + S(x_2)[P_{22}] = [Q_2]$$

where

$$[P_{11}] = [1] - \tau[\diagdown^{A_{11}}][B], \qquad [P_{21}] = \tau[\diagdown^{A_{21}}][B]$$
$$[P_{12}] = \tau[\diagdown^{A_{12}}][B], \qquad [P_{22}] = [1] - \tau[\diagdown^{A_{22}}][B]$$
$$[Q_1] = x_1(0)[1, 1, \ldots] + \tau[C_1][B]$$
$$[Q_2] = x_2(0)[1, 1, 1, \ldots] + \tau[C_2][B]$$

Then

$$S(x_1) = [Q_1 P_{12}{}^{-1} - Q_2 P_{22}{}^{-1}] * [P_{11}P_{12}{}^{-1} - P_{21}P_{22}{}^{-1}]$$
$$S(x_2) = [Q_1 P_{11}{}^{-1} - Q_2 P_{21}{}^{-1}] * [P_{12}P_{11}{}^{-1} - P_{22}P_{21}{}^{-1}]$$

(See Problem 5.4, Appendix.)

EXAMPLE 5.5

Consider the two equations

$$x_1 = a_{11}x_1 + a_{12}x_2 + C_1(t)$$
$$\dot{x}_2 = a_{21}x_1 + a_{22}x_2 + C_2(t)$$
$$[P_{11}] = [1] - \tau[\diagdown^{A_{11}}][B] = [1 - 0.5\tau a_{11}, -a_{11}\tau, -a_{11}\tau, \ldots]$$
$$[P_{12}] = [\diagdown^{A_{12}}][B] = a_{12}\tau[0.5, 1, 1, 1, \ldots]$$
$$[P_{21}] = [\diagdown^{A_{21}}][B] = a_{21}\tau[0.5, 1, 1, 1, \ldots]$$
$$[P_{22}] = [1] - \tau[\diagdown^{A_{22}}][B] = [1 - 0.5\tau a_{22}, -a_{22}\tau, -a_{22}\tau, \ldots]$$

$$[Q_1] = \frac{\tau}{2}(x_1(0) + C_1(0))[1, 1, 1, \ldots] + \tau S(C_1) * [0.5, 1, 1, 1, \ldots]$$

$$[Q_2] = \frac{\tau}{2}(x_2(0) + C_2(0))[1, 1, 1, \ldots] + \tau S(C_2) * [0.5, 1, 1, 1, \ldots]$$

$$S(x_1) = \left\{ \frac{(\tau/2)(x_1(0) + C_1(0))[1, 1, 1, \ldots] + \tau S(C_1) * [0.5, 1, 1, 1, \ldots]}{[1 - a_{11}(0.5\tau), -a_{11}\tau, -a_{11}\tau, -a_{11}\tau, \ldots]} \right.$$
$$\left. - \frac{(\tau/2)(x_2(0) + C_2(0))[1, 1, 1, \ldots] + \tau S(C_2) * [0.5, 1, 1, 1, \ldots]}{[1 - a_{22}(0.5\tau), -a_{22}\tau, -a_{22}\tau, -a_{22}\tau, \ldots]} \right\}$$
$$\overset{*}{\underset{*}{*}} \left\{ \frac{[1 - a_{11}(0.5\tau), -a_{11}\tau, -a_{11}\tau, \ldots]}{a_{12}\tau[0.5, 1, 1, 1, \ldots]} \right.$$
$$\left. - \frac{a_{21}\tau[0.5, 1, 1, 1, \ldots]}{[1 - a_{22}(0.5\tau), -a_{22}\tau, -a_{22}\tau, \ldots]} \right\}$$

5.3.2 Multivariable Control System Identification

Consider the system A shown in Fig. 5.19, with m and n load variables (independent), w, x, and y controlled variables, R_w, R_x, and R_y controllers.

The analytical study of such processes is very difficult, and impulse analysis can be used with advantage in solving the two following problems:

1. Determination of the dynamic characteristics of the process
2. Determination of the variations of the different controlled variables resulting from a given variation of the load or input variables

To determine experimentally the dynamic characteristics of a multivariable system, it is necessary to open the feedback loops as shown in Fig.

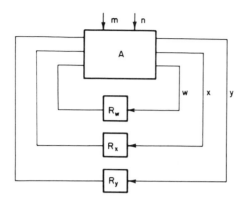

FIG. **5.19** Block diagram of a multivariable control system.

5.20, where w^*, x^*, y^* are independent variables corresponding to w, x, y and are the input of the controllers R_w, R_x, R_y.

A way to determine the impulse responses G_{mx}, G_{ny}, G_{wx}, G_{yx}, G_{xx} is to keep all but one variable m, n, w^*, x^*, y^* constant. For example, record the variation of m and the corresponding variation of x. The sequence of the impulse response G_{mx} is given by the operation of deconvolution applied to the sequence $S(x)$ and $S(m)$

$$S(G_{mx}) = \frac{1}{\tau} \frac{S(x)}{S_i(m)}$$

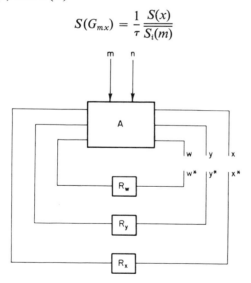

FIG. **5.20** Schematic of a controlled system with many degrees of freedom.

Usually it is not possible to keep all but one variable constant. However, it may be possible to measure a variation $x_1(t)$ resulting from the simultaneous variation $m_1(t)$ and $n_1(t)$ of the load variable m and n, and at another time a variation $x_2(t)$ resulting from $m_2(t)$ and $n_2(t)$.

If the system is linear, we can add the variations resulting from each load variable m and n and we may write

$$S(x_1) = S(m_1) * S(G_{mx}) + S(n_1) * S(G_{nx})$$
$$S(x_2) = S(m_2) * S(G_{mx}) + S(n_2) * S(G_{nx})$$

with

G_{mx} = impulse response of x with regard to a variation of m

G_{nx} = impulse response of x with regard to a variation of n

In this way we obtain a system of two equations with the two unknown sequences $S(G_{mx})$ and $S(G_{nx})$. If we solve this system we obtain (see problem 11.2, Appendix)

$$S(G_{mx}) = \frac{\begin{vmatrix} S(x_1) & S(n_1) \\ S(x_2) & S(n_2) \end{vmatrix}}{\begin{vmatrix} S(m_1) & S(n_1) \\ S(m_2) & S(n_2) \end{vmatrix}}$$

$$= \frac{(Sx_1) * S(n_2) - S(x_2) * S(n_1)}{S(m_1) * S(n_2) - S(m_2) * S(n_1)}$$

and

$$S(G_{nx}) = \frac{S(m_1) * S(x_2) - S(m_2) * S(x_1)}{S(m_1) * S(n_2) - S(m_2) * S(n_1)}$$

In the general case of a system with k inputs, we have

$$S(G_{nx}) = \frac{\begin{vmatrix} S(x_1) & S(n_1) & \cdots & S(k_1) \\ S(x_2) & S(n_2) & \cdots & S(k_2) \\ & & \vdots & \\ S(x_k) & S(n_k) & \cdots & S(k_k) \end{vmatrix}}{\begin{vmatrix} S(m_1) & S(n_1) & \cdots & S(k_1) \\ S(m_2) & S(n_2) & \cdots & S(k_2) \\ & & \vdots & \\ S(m_k) & S(n_k) & \cdots & S(k_k) \end{vmatrix}} \tag{5.4}$$

After performing the convolution and deconvolution operations involved in this quotient of determinants, it is possible to determine the impulse response with any number of variables.

5.3.3   Multivariable Control System Response to Deterministic Inputs

Suppose that the different impulse responses of the system are known. Suppose also that the feedback loops are open and the system is linear. We obtain

$$S(x) = S(m) * S(G_{mx}) + S(n) * S(G_{nx}) + \cdots$$
$$+ S(x^*) * S(G_{xx}) + S(y^*)S(G_{yx}) + \cdots$$
$$S(y) = S(m) * S(G_{my}) + S(n) * S(G_{ny}) + \cdots$$
$$+ S(x^*) * S(G_{xy}) + S(y^*) * S(G_{yy}) + \cdots$$

If the feedback loops are closed, we can write

$$S(x) = S(x^*), \qquad S(y) = S(y^*), \ldots$$

and we obtain

$$S(x) * [S(G_{xx}) - [1]] + S(y) * S(G_{yx}) + \cdots$$
$$= -(S(m) * S(G_{mx}) + S(n) * S(G_{nx}) + \cdots)$$
$$S(x) * S(G_{xy}) + S(y) * [S(G_{yy}) - [1]] + \cdots$$
$$= -(S(m) * S(G_{my}) + S(n) * S(G_{ny}) + \cdots)$$

We can solve this system with regard to the unknown sequences $S(x)$, $S(y) \cdots$ and, for $S(x)$, for instance, obtain

$$S(x) = \frac{\begin{vmatrix} -[S(m) * S(G_{mx}) + S(n) * S(G_{nx})] & S(G_{yx}) \cdots \\ -[S(m) * S(G_{my}) + S(n) * S(G_{ny})] & S(G_{yy}) - [1] \cdots \\ \vdots & \vdots \end{vmatrix}}{\begin{vmatrix} S(G_{xx}) - [1] & S(G_{yx}) \cdots \\ S(G_{xy}) & S(G_{yy}) - [1] \cdots \\ \vdots & \vdots \end{vmatrix}} \tag{5.5}$$

SPECIAL CASES

a. *Systems with One Control Variable*

The system of operations becomes

$$S(x) * [S(G_{xx}) - [1]] = -S(m) * S(G_{mx})$$
$$S(x) = -\frac{S(m) * S(G_{mx})}{S(G_{xx}) - [1]} = \frac{S(m) * S(G_{mx})}{[1] - S(G_{xx})}$$

which is the previously obtained result.

b. *Systems with Two Control Variables*

$$S(x) = \frac{\begin{vmatrix} -S(m) * S(G_{mx}) & S(G_{yx}) \\ -S(m) * S(G_{my}) & S(G_{yy}) - [1] \end{vmatrix}}{\begin{vmatrix} S(G_{xx}) - [1] & S(G_{yx}) \\ S(G_{xy}) & S(G_{yy}) - [1] \end{vmatrix}}$$

$$S(x) = \frac{S(m) * \{S(G_{mx}) * [S(G_{yy}) - [1]] - S(G_{my}) * S(G_{yx})\}}{[S(G_{xx}) - [1]] * [S(G_{yy}) - [1]] - S(G_{yx}) * S(G_{xy})}$$

If the sequences $S(m)$, $S(G_{mx})$, $S(G_{my})$, $S(G_{xx})$, $S(G_{yy})$ are known, it is not difficult to determine the sequences of the numerator and denominator of this expression and the variation $x(t)$ resulting from a given variation of the load variable m. This computation would be very difficult using the classical methods, especially if the analytical expression of m, G_{mx}, G_{my}, G_{xx}, and G_{yy} are not known. With the help of impulse analysis and a digital computer the computation is straightforward.

5.4 SYSTEM IDENTIFICATION

In Sec. 2.3.2 it was demonstrated that the impulse response of a linear system may be determined by the deconvolution operation. In Sec. 2.3.3 it was demonstrated that deconvolution may be applied to nonlinear systems to obtain an indication of system performance and the effect of the non-linearity. This section is devoted to the presentation of several system identification techniques using impulse analysis.

5.4.1 System Identification through Deconvolution

Linear systems may be identified merely by observing the impulse, step, or frequency response. However, frequently a step input may not be applied and the only data available are input and output records. If, for the system shown in Fig. 5.21, the input and output are approximately in the steady state at some time $t = t_0$, we may consider only $x(t) = x_i(t) - x_i(t_0)$ and $y(t) = y_0(t) - y_0(t_0)$.

For this case, by deconvolution, we have the impulse response

$$S_i(G) = \frac{1}{\tau} \frac{S(Y)}{S_i(X)}$$

and the step response

$$S(y) = \tau S_i(G) * [1, 1, 1, \dots]$$

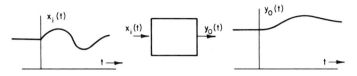

FIG. **5.21** System identification.

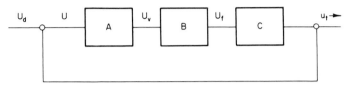

FIG. **5.22** Functional diagram of the voltage regulator of an alternator. A, voltage controller and amplifier; B, primary exciter; C, alternator circuit; u_t, terminal voltage of generator (control variable); u_d, set point of generator voltage; u_v, excitation voltage at the exciter; u_f, excitation voltage at the alternator.

or

$$S(\gamma) = \frac{S(Y) * [1, 1, 1, \ldots]}{S_i(X)} = \frac{S(Y)}{S_i(X) * [1, -1]} \tag{5.6}$$

EXAMPLE 5.6

See Example 2.12.

EXAMPLE 5.7

The technique used above has been applied to determine the dynamic characteristics of a voltage control system (see Laible [21]). Figure 5.22(a) is the block diagram of the system.

Figure 5.22(b) gives the measured variation of u, u_f, and u_v after a connection of a tie-line load of 69.5 Mvar. The time interval τ was chosen as $\tau = 0.1$. From Fig. 5.23(a) we obtain the sequences

$S_i(u) = [0.207, 0.307, 0.351, 0.358, 0.330, 0.283,$
$\qquad 0.223, 0.163, 0.103, 0.045, -0.001, -0.030,$
$\qquad -0.034, -0.030, -0.019, -0.002, 0.010, 0.020, \ldots]$

$S(u_f) = [0.052, 0.418, 1.046, 2.61, 3.81, 4.46,$
$\qquad 0.46, 4.19, 3.72, 3.07, 2.26, 1.445,$
$\qquad 0.382, 0.505, 0.426, 0.515, 0.635, 0.702, \ldots]$

$S(u_v) = [3.33, 11.0, 17.07, 16.4, 12.8, 6.74,$
$\qquad 0.80, -3.04, -4.95, -5.95, -5.63, -4.13,$
$\qquad -2.16, 0.36, 2.08, 2.46, 1.87, \ldots]$

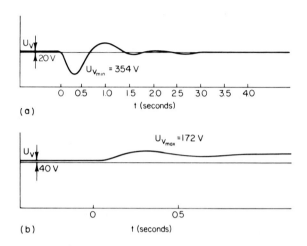

(a)

(b)

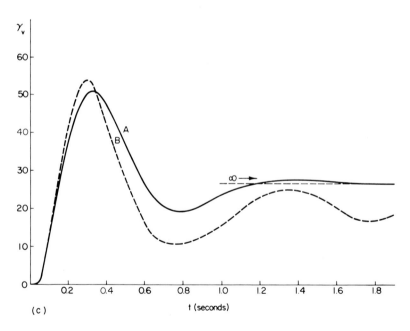

(c)

FIG. **5.23** (a) and (b) Measured variation of voltage control system. (c) Plotted step response of the voltage regulator system and the principal and auxiliary excitations; curve *A*, calculated response curve; *B*, measured response.

To obtain the step response of the system A with input u and output u_v,

$$S(\gamma_A) = \tau S(g_A) * [1, 1, 1, \ldots] = \frac{S(u_v) * [1, 1, 1, \ldots]}{S_i(u)}$$

thus,

$$S(\gamma_A) = [0, 16.1, 45.36, 57.13, 41.44, 30.32, 16.95, 10.52,$$
$$11.91, 15.37, 16.34, 20.16, 24.39, 25.47, 26.98, 24.86, \ldots]$$

This resultant step response is plotted in Fig. 5.23(c) and compared with the actual measured step response taken from Fig. 5.23(b).

5.4.2 Determination of System Frequency Response from the Time Response

Dynamic processes are generally described by their frequency response. The frequency characteristics are used to investigate system performance and stability. Thus it is desirable to be able to evaluate the frequency response of a system or process from its time series data.

Consider a linear system with input $x(t)$, output $y(t)$, step response $\gamma(t)$, and transfer function

$$H(j\omega) = j\omega \int_0^\infty \gamma(t) e^{-j\omega t}\, dt$$

Integrating twice by parts,

$$H(j\omega) = \frac{1}{j\omega} \int_0^\infty e^{-j\omega t}\, \ddot{\gamma}(t)\, dt + \gamma(0) + \frac{\dot{\gamma}(0)}{j\omega} - \lim_{T \to \infty} \left[e^{-j\omega T} \left(\gamma(T) + \frac{\dot{\gamma}(T)}{j\omega} \right) \right]$$

provided the integral and the limit on the right exist. Thus

$$H(j\omega) = R(j\omega) + jI(j\omega)$$

where

$$R(j\omega) = -\frac{1}{\omega} \int_0^\infty \ddot{\gamma}(t) \sin \omega t\, dt + \gamma(0) + \lim_{T \to \infty} \left[\frac{\dot{\gamma}(T)}{\omega} \sin \omega T - \gamma(T) \cos \omega T \right]$$

and

$$I(j\omega) = -\frac{1}{\omega} \int_0^\infty \ddot{\gamma}(t) \cos \omega t\, dt - \frac{\dot{\gamma}(0)}{\omega} + \lim_{T \to \infty} \left[\frac{\dot{\gamma}(T)}{\omega} \cos \omega T + \gamma(T) \sin \omega T \right]$$

if

$$\lim_{T \to \infty} \gamma(T) = \lim_{T \to \infty} \dot{\gamma}(T) = 0$$

The real and imaginary parts of $H(j\omega)$ may be determined by

$$R(j\omega) = -\frac{1}{\omega} \int_0^\infty \ddot{\gamma}(t) \sin \omega t \, dt + \gamma(0)$$

$$\approx -\frac{1}{\omega} S(\ddot{\gamma}(t) \sin \omega t) * \frac{\tau}{2} \begin{bmatrix} 1, 1 \\ 1, -1 \end{bmatrix} + \gamma_0$$

where

$$S(\ddot{\gamma}) = \frac{1}{T^2} [S(\gamma) * [1, -2, 1]]D(1) + \frac{2\gamma_2 - 3\gamma_1}{T^2}$$

(See Problem 2.10, Appendix.)

Also

$$I(j\omega) = -\frac{1}{\omega} \int_0^\infty \ddot{\gamma}(t) \cos \omega t \, dt - \frac{\dot{\gamma}(0)}{\omega}$$

$$\approx -\frac{1}{\omega} S(\ddot{\gamma}(t) \cos \omega t) * \frac{\tau}{2} \begin{bmatrix} 1, 1 \\ 1, -1 \end{bmatrix} - \frac{2\gamma_1 - \gamma_2}{\tau}$$

(See Sec. 2.5.)

If $\lim_{T \to \infty} \gamma(T) \neq 0$, the integral $\int_0^\infty e^{-j\omega t} \gamma(t) \, dt$ does not necessarily converge. However, if $\gamma(t)$ is of exponential order α_0 (that is,

$$\lim_{T \to \infty} \gamma(T) e^{-\alpha T} = 0$$

for all $\alpha > \alpha_0$), the integral

$$\int_0^\infty e^{-(\alpha + j\omega)t} \gamma(t) \, dt$$

converges for $\alpha > \alpha_0$. Letting $s = \alpha + j\omega$, the transfer function

$$H(s) = \frac{1}{s} \int_0^\infty \gamma(t) e^{-sT} \, dt$$

may be integrated twice by parts to obtain for Re $(s) > \alpha_0$:†

$$H(s) = \frac{1}{s} \int_0^\infty \ddot{\gamma}(t) e^{-sT} \, dt + \gamma(0) + \frac{\dot{\gamma}(0)}{s}$$

---

† It is assumed that $\dot{\gamma}(t)$ is continuous for $t > 0$ and has a limit at $t = 0$. $\dot{\gamma}(t)$ is of exponential order α_0 for some $\alpha_0 < \infty$, but $\ddot{\gamma}(t)$ need not be of exponential order (see Theorem 10–9 of Lepage [22]).

Thus, for all $\gamma(t)$ satisfying these conditions,† the frequency response is

$$H(j\omega) = \frac{1}{j\omega} \int_0^\infty e^{-j\omega t} \ddot{\gamma}(t) \, dt + \gamma(0) + \frac{\dot{\gamma}(0)}{j\omega} \tag{5.7}$$

EXAMPLE 5.8†

Figure 5.24(a) represents the step response of a linear system. To determine an analytical expression for the transfer function, we first compute the frequency response $H(j\omega)$ by the procedure outlined above.

Choosing $\tau = 5$ s and computing $R(j\omega)$ and $I(j\omega)$ for various values of ω, we obtain the polar plot of $H(j\omega)$ shown in Fig. 5.24(b).

Since the polar plot of $H(j\omega)$ passes through three quadrants and is reasonably smooth, it appears that the system may be approximated quite well by the transfer function

$$H(s) = \frac{K}{(T_1s + 1)(T_2s + 1)(T_3s + 1)}$$

The time constants T_1, T_2, and T_3 may be determined as the reciprocal of the corner frequencies ω_1, ω_2, and ω_3 in the Bode plot of $|H(j\omega)|$ in Fig. 5.24(c) to yield $|H(j\omega)|$.

Precise calculations of the time constants may be obtained by minimizing the difference between $H(j\omega)$ and the calculated values of $H(j\omega)$ in a mean square sense or any other reasonable criterion.

5.4.3 Tsypkin's Method

To the system shown in Fig. 5.25(a) we apply an arbitrary input that is removed at what may be called time $t = 0$. Figure 5.25(b) and (c) represent this input and the resultant response. The sequence $S(Y)$ is evaluated for $t \geq 0$.

$$S(Y) = [y_0, y_1, y_2, \ldots, y_n, y_{n+1}, y_{n+2}, \ldots]$$

Assume that the system may be described by the second-order differential equation

$$(T_2{}^2s^2 + T_1s + 1)y(s) = Kx(s)$$

It is required to determine T_1 and T_2(K is the static gain). This equation has the solution

$$y(t) = C_1e^{s_1t} + C_2e^{s_2t}$$

---

† See Unbehauen [46].

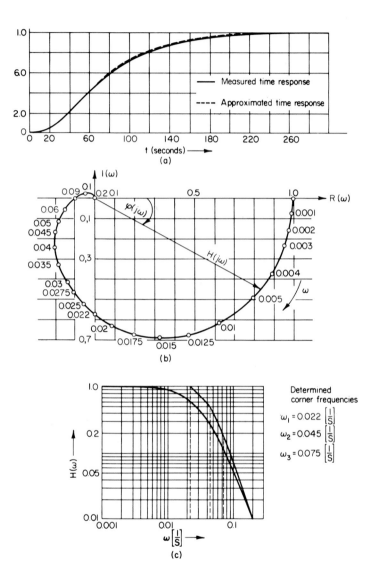

FIG. **5.24**   System response. (a) Step response. (b) Frequency response. (c) Frequency response.

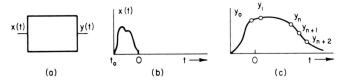

FIG. **5.25** Tsypkin's method.

where

$$s_1, s_2 = -\frac{T_1}{2T_2^2} \pm j\frac{1}{T_2}\sqrt{\frac{T_1}{2} - 1} = -\alpha \pm j\omega$$

Taking three adjacent values of $S(Y)$, we have

$$y_n = C_1 e^{s_1 n\tau} + C_2 e^{s_2 n\tau}$$
$$y_{n+1} = C_1 e^{s_1(n+1)\tau} + C_2 e^{s_2(n+1)\tau}$$
$$y_{n+2} = C_1 e^{s_1(n+2)\tau} + C_2 e^{s_2(n+2)\tau}$$

Eliminating the constants C_1 and C_2 yields

$$y_{n+2} - (e^{s_1\tau} + e^{s_2\tau})y_{n+1} + e^{(s_1+s_2)\tau} y_n = 0$$

or

$$\frac{y_{n+2}}{y_n} = b\frac{y_{n+1}}{y_n} - c$$

where

$$b = e^{s_1\tau} + e^{s_2\tau} \quad \text{and} \quad c = e^{(s_1+s_2)\tau}$$

which is the equation of a straight line. For each triplet of values, the point $(y_{n+2}/y_n, y_{n+1}/y_n)$ is plotted as in Fig. 5.26, and the regression line that is the best fit through the points describes the system, since

$$\cos \omega\tau = \frac{b}{2\sqrt{c}} \quad \text{and} \quad \alpha = -\frac{\ln c}{2\tau}$$

and

$$T_2^2 = \frac{1}{\alpha^2 + \omega^2} \quad \text{and} \quad T_1 = 2\alpha T_2^2$$

If the regression line passes through the origin, then the equation of the system is

$$\left(-\frac{\tau}{\ln b}s + 1\right)Y(s) = kX(s)$$

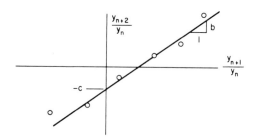

Fig. **5.26** Tsypkin's method.

EXAMPLE 5.9

To demonstrate the validity of the method, we evaluate the exact impulse response of the system

$$(T_2{}^2 s^2 + T_1 s + 1) Y(s) = X(s) = 1 \qquad \text{for } T_1 = T_2 = 1$$

which yields

$$y(t) = e^{-t/2}\left(\cos \frac{\sqrt{3}}{2} t + \frac{\sqrt{3}}{3} \sin \frac{\sqrt{3}}{2} t\right) u(t)$$

For $\tau = 1/2$,

$$S(Y) = [1, 0.896, 0.660, 0.390, 0.151, -0.0234, -0.124,$$
$$-0.162, -0.153, -0.118, \ldots]$$

Figure 5.27 is a plot of the points $(y_{n+2}/y_n, y_{n+1}/y_n)$.

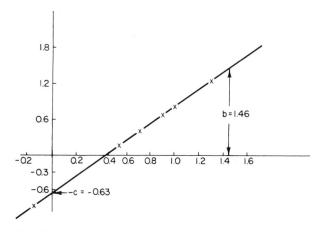

Fig. **5.27** Example 5.9, application of Tsypkin's method.

From the line through the points we have

$$b = 1.46, \qquad c = 0.63$$

$$\alpha = \frac{-\ln c}{2\tau} = -\ln 0.63 = 0.412$$

$$\omega\tau = \cos^{-1}\frac{b}{2\sqrt{C}} = \cos^{-1} 0.919 = 0.409, \qquad \omega = 0.818$$

$$T_2 = \sqrt{\frac{1}{\alpha^2 + \omega^2}} = 1.06, \qquad T_1 = 2\alpha T_2^2 = 1.04$$

In general, if the points all lie near the regression line, the system is approximately a second-order system and if c is also approximately zero, the system may be approximated by a first-order system. Alternatively, if the points do not fall in a linear fashion, the system may not be approximated (well) by a second-order system.

5.4.4 Identification of Processes with Random Inputs

Given a linear system with impulse response $g(t)$ and stationary random input and output $x(t)$ and $y(t)$, respectively, the cross-correlation function $R_{xy}(\theta)$ and the autocorrelation function of the input $R_{xx}(\theta)$ are related by the equation

$$R_{xy}(\theta) = \int_0^\infty R_{xx}(\theta - \tau)g(\tau)\, d\tau$$

which is pictured in Fig. 5.28.

Suppose that $R_{xy}(\theta) \approx R_{xx}(\theta) \approx 0$ for $|\theta| > \theta_0$. Then we may define the sequences

$$S(Z) = S(R_{xy}(\theta)) = [z_{-k}, z_{-k+1}, z_{-k+2}, \ldots, z_{-1}, z_0, z_1, \ldots, z_k]$$
$$S(X) = S(R_{xx}(\theta)) = [x_{-k}, x_{-k+1}, x_{-k+2}, \ldots, x_{-1}, x_0, x_1, \ldots, x_k]$$

and

$$S(Z) = \tau S(X) * S(G)$$

Thus

$$S(G) = \frac{1}{\tau}\frac{S(Z)}{S(X)} = \frac{1}{\tau}\frac{S(R_{xy}(\theta))}{S(R_{xx}(\theta))} \tag{5.8}$$

(See Sec. 2.3.1.)

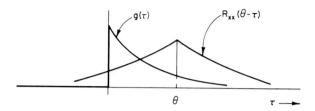

FIG. **5.28** Identification from autocorrelation.

Usually the values of $R_{xx}(\theta)$ and $R_{xy}(\theta)$ are most accurate for small θ. We have seen that the deconvolution is particularly sensitive to inaccuracies in the first few terms of the sequences being deconvoluted. Thus it is to be expected that poor results will be obtained by using the deconvolution as proposed above, since the functions are most inaccurate near $\theta = -\theta_0$ and inaccuracies are exaggerated by the truncation of $R_{xx}(\theta)$ and $R_{xy}(\theta)$.

It was demonstrated in Sec. 2.3.1 that if we define

$$S(Z) = [z_0, z_1, z_2, \ldots]$$

then

$$S(Z) = \tau S(G)A$$

where A is given in Sec. 2.3.1. Thus

$$S(G) = \frac{1}{\tau} S(Z)A^{-1}$$

Note that the evaluation of $S(G)$ is not particularly sensitive to the truncation of $S(Z)$ and $S(X)$. Also, the terms x_k and $z_k \doteq 0$, so the operation is not greatly affected by these values. In fact, $S(G)$ depends most upon the most accurate values of $R_{xx}(\theta)$ and $R_{xy}(\theta)$ near $\theta = 0$.

EXAMPLE 5.10

Consider the case

$$g(t) = \tfrac{1}{2}e^{-(t/2)}u(t), \qquad R_{xx}(\theta) = e^{-|\theta|})$$
$$R_{xx}(\theta) = e^{-|\theta|}, \qquad R_{yy}(\theta) = \tfrac{4}{3}e^{-|\theta|} - e^{-|\theta|}$$

With $\tau = 1/2$ and $\theta_0 = 13/2$, we have

$$S(X) = [x_0, x_1, x_2, \ldots, x_{13}]$$
$$= [1, 0.606, 0.368, 0.223, 0.135, 0.082, \ldots]$$

$$S(Z) = [z_0, z_1, z_2, \ldots, z_{13}]$$
$$= [0.333, 0.432, 0.441, 0.407, 0.355, 0.300, \ldots]$$

and

$$S(G) = \frac{1}{\tau} S(Z)A^{-1}$$
$$= [0.452, 0.383, 0.299, 0.233, 0.181, 0.141, \ldots]$$

The results of this operation are compared with the results of Problem 5.14 (Appendix) and the exact impulse response in Table 5.2. Note that even with the increment size τ equal to the time constant of the system, this method gives an error less than 10 percent.

TABLE 5.2

t	Exact $\frac{1}{2}e^{-(t/2)}$	$\frac{1}{\tau}S(Z)A^{-1}$	$\frac{1}{\tau}\frac{S(Z)}{S(X)}$
0	0.50000	0.45175	33.462
τ	0.38940	0.38345	−12.719
2τ	0.30327	0.29862	−16.110
3τ	0.23619	0.23261	−20.571
4τ	0.18374	0.18111	−26.467
5τ	0.14325	0.14107	−34.143
6τ	0.11157	0.10987	−43.646
7τ	0.08689	0.08552	−56.167
8τ	0.06767	0.06666	−71.958
9τ	0.05270	0.05191	−93.054
10τ	0.04104	0.04038	−118.812
11τ	0.03197	0.03148	−152.891
12τ	0.02490	0.02453	−196.241
13τ	0.01939	0.03617	−252.063

5.5 NONLINEAR CONTROL SYSTEMS†

Consider the block diagram of the nonlinear control system shown in Fig. 5.29, where

ϕ = nonlinear element (independent of time)
$g(t)$ = impulse response of linear element
$x(t)$ = controlled variable
$k(t)$ = input (or load) variable
$z(t)$ = error = $k(t) - x(t)$

† The fundamentals of this method were developed in the United States by T. M. Stout [40] and in the U.S.S.R. by B. Naumov [26].

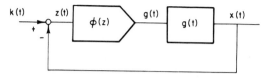

FIG. **5.29**   Nonlinear system.

$y = \phi(z)$ is the relationship between the input z and the output y of the nonlinear element. The relationships among k, z, y, and x are

$$z(t) = k(t) - x(t)$$

$$y(t) = \phi(z(t))$$

$$x(t) = \int_0^t g(t - \tau)y(\tau)\,d\tau$$

Thus

$$z(t) = k(t) - \int_0^t g(t - \tau)\phi(z(\tau))\,d\tau$$

or

$$S(z) = S(k) - S(x) = S(k) - \tau S(g) * S(\phi)$$

where

$$\phi_n = \phi(z_n)$$

The general term (x_n) of the convolution (by the trapezoidal rule) is

$$x_n = \tau\left[\frac{g_0\phi_n}{2} + g_1\phi_{n-1} + \cdots + g_{n-1}\phi_1 + \frac{g_n\phi_0}{2}\right]$$

where

$$\phi_0 = \phi(z(0)) = \phi(z_0)$$
$$\phi_1 = \phi(z(\tau)) = \phi(z_1)$$
$$\phi_n = \phi(z(n\tau)) = \phi(z_n)$$

Introducing this expression into the equation for $S(z)$, we have for the general term,

$$z_n = k_n - \tau\left[\frac{g_0\phi_n}{2} + g_1\phi_{n-1} + \cdots + \frac{g_n\phi_0}{2}\right]$$

which is a system of $n + 1$ equations with the $n + 1$ unknowns $z_0, z_1, z_2, \ldots,$ z_n. Setting $\phi_n = z_n$ for every n yields the recurrence equation obtained for linear systems.

If $g_0 = 0$, the above recurrence relations may easily be solved successively for the z_n, since the equation becomes

$$z_n = k_n - \tau\left[g_1\phi_{n-1} + g_2\phi_{n-2} + \cdots + \frac{g_n\phi_0}{2}\right] \tag{5.9}$$

For this case ($g_0 = 0$) the input to the nonlinear element does not depend upon the instantaneous values of $y(t)$. That is, there is a delay of at least one sample in the loop. This allows direct computation of z_n from only past values of $k(t)$ and $x(t)$.

For this system we have

$$z_0 = 0$$
$$z_1 = k_1 - \tau\tfrac{1}{2}g_1\phi_0 = k_1 - \Sigma_1{}^*$$
$$z_2 = k_2 - \tau(g_1\phi_1 + \tfrac{1}{2}g_2\phi_2) = k_2 - \Sigma_2{}^*$$
$$\vdots$$
$$z_n = k_n - \tau(g_1\phi_{n-1} + g_2\phi_{n-2} + \cdots + \tfrac{1}{2}g_n\phi)$$

(Note that the last term of $\Sigma_n{}^*$ contains the factor $\tfrac{1}{2}$.)

We may solve this system by a table similar to that used for linear systems. We need only add the step of calculating (or looking up in a reference) $\phi(z_n)$ when z_n is determined as shown in the following tabular algorithm.

n	k_n	$x_n = \Sigma_n{}^*$	$z_n = k_n - x_n$	$y_n = \phi(z_n)$	τg_1	τg_2	τg_3	τg_4	$\cdots$
0	k_0	x_0	$z_0 = x_0$	ϕ_0	$\tau g_1\dfrac{\phi_0}{2}$	$\tau g_2\dfrac{\phi_0}{2}$	$\tau g_3\dfrac{\phi_0}{2}$	$\tau g_4\dfrac{\phi_0}{2}$	$\cdots$
1	k_1	$x_1 = \Sigma_1{}^*$	$z_1 = k_1 - x_1$	ϕ_1	$\Sigma_1{}^*$	$\tau g_1\phi_1$	$\tau g_2\phi_1$	$\tau g_3\phi_1$	$\cdots$
2	k_2	$x_2 = \Sigma_2{}^*$	$z_2 = k_2 - x_2$	ϕ_2		$\Sigma_2{}^*$	$\tau g_1\phi_2$	$\tau g_2\phi_2$	$\cdots$
3	k_3	$x_3 = \Sigma_3{}^*$	$z_3 = k_3 - x_3$	ϕ_3			$\Sigma_3{}^*$	$\tau g_1\phi_3$	$\cdots$
4	k_4	$x_4 = \Sigma_4{}^*$	$z_4 = k_4 - x_4$	ϕ_4				$\Sigma_4{}^*$	
5	k_5	$\vdots$	$\vdots$	$\vdots$					

$$\Sigma_1{}^* = \tau g_1 \frac{\phi_0}{2} = x_1$$

$$\Sigma_2{}^* = \tau\left(g_1\phi_1 + g_2\frac{\phi_0}{2}\right) = x_2$$

$$\Sigma_3{}^* = \tau\left(g_1\phi_2 + g_2\phi_1 + g_3\frac{\phi_0}{2}\right) = x_3$$

$$\vdots$$

$$\Sigma_n{}^* = \tau\left(g_1\phi_{n-1} + g_2\phi_{n-2} + \cdots + g_n\frac{\phi_0}{2}\right) = x_n$$

An outline of the procedure is as follows:

1. Determine the sequence of the impulse response of the linear portion of the control loop

$$S(g) = [0, g_1, g_2, g_3, \ldots]$$

2. Determine the nonlinear relation $y = \phi(z)$, this may be given by a curve or recorded data.

3. Determine $z_0 = k_0 - x_0$.

4. Determine $\phi_0 = \phi(z_0)$.

5. Prepare the table.

6. Fill in first row with the products

$$\tau g_1 \frac{\phi_0}{2}, \qquad \tau g_2 \frac{\phi_0}{2}, \qquad \tau g_3 \frac{\phi_0}{2}, \ldots$$

7. Determine

$$z_1 = k - \Sigma_1^* = k_1 - \tau g_1 \frac{\phi_0}{2}$$

8. Determine

$$\phi_1 = \phi(z_1)$$

It is usually easier in hand calculation to tabulate $\phi(z)$ for the range of z of interest (or suspected interest). Frequently, $\phi(z)$ is given in a graphical rather than analytical representation. For use on a digital computer the tabulation is, of course, entered into memory for recall and interpolation.

If the input $k(t)$ is not applied to the nonlinear element, an additional step must be included to determine $z(t)$. (See Fig. 5.30.)

$$G_R(s) = G_A(s)G_B(s)$$

We must use the procedure given above to find $S(\omega)$ by

$$S(z) = \tau S(\omega)S(g_R)$$

$$\omega_n = k_n - y_n$$

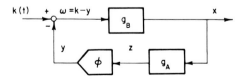

FIG. **5.30**   Nonlinear feedback system.

Then

$$S(x) = \tau S(\omega) + S(g_B)$$

EXAMPLE 5.11

Consider the systems shown in Fig. 5.29, where

$$g(t) = \frac{t}{T^2} u(t) \quad \text{and} \quad k(t) = u(t)$$

and

$$y(t) = \phi(z) = z \quad \text{(linear system)}$$

For this case we have the known solution

$$x(t) = \left(1 - \cos\frac{t}{T}\right)u(t)$$

Setting up the table, we have ($T = \tau = 1$)

$$S(G) = [0, 1, 2, 3, \ldots]$$

n	k_n	$x_n = \sum_n{}^*$	$z_n = k_n - x_n$	$y_n = \phi_n$	$\tau g_1 = 1$	$\tau g_2 = 2$	$\tau g_3 = 3$	$\tau g_4 = 4$	$\tau g_5 = 5$	$\tau g_6 = 6$	$\cdots$
0	1	0	1	1	0.5	1	1.5	2	2.5	3	$\cdots$
1	1	0.5	0.5	0.5	0.5	0.5	1	1.5	2	2.5	$\cdots$
2	1	1.5	-0.5	-0.5		1.5	-0.5	-1	-1.5	-2	$\cdots$
3	1	2	-1	-1			2	-1	-2	-3	$\cdots$
4	1	1.5	-0.5	-0.5				1	-0.5	-1	$\cdots$
5	1	0.5	0.5	0.5					0.5	$\cdot$	$\cdots$
$\vdots$	$\vdots$	$\vdots$	$\vdots$	$\vdots$						$\vdots$	

Thus

$$S(x) = [0, 0.5, 1.5, 2, 1.5, 0.5, 0, 0.5, \ldots]$$

which approximates the exact sequence quite closely.

Now consider the nonlinear element

$$y = \phi(z) = z^2 \, \text{sgn} \, z = \begin{cases} -z^2 & \text{for } z < 0 \\ 0 & \text{for } z = 0 \\ +z^2 & \text{for } z > 0 \end{cases}$$

For this situation we need only perform the additional step $y_n = \phi(z_n)$ in the accompanying table.

n	k_n	x_n	z_n	$y_n = \phi(z)_n$	1	2	3	4	5	6	7	$\cdots$
0	1	0	1	1	0.5	1	1.5	2	2.5	3	3.5	$\cdots$
1	1	0.5	0.5	0.25	0.5	0.25	0.5	0.75	1	1.25	1.5	$\cdots$
2	1	1.25	-0.25	-0.0625		1.25	-0.0625	-0.125	-0.1875	-0.25	-0.3125	$\cdots$
3	1	1.9375	-0.9375	-0.88			1.9375	-0.88	-1.76	-2.64	-3.52	$\cdots$
4	1	1.745	-0.745	-0.56				1.745	-0.56	-1.12	-1.68	$\cdots$
5	1	0.9925	0	0					0.9925	0	0	$\cdots$
6	1	0.24	0.76	0.58						0.24	0.58	$\cdots$
7	1	0.0675	$\cdots$	$\cdots$							0.0675	$\cdots$

Thus $S(x) = [0, 0.5, 1.25, 1.9375, 1.745, 0.9925, 0.240, 0.0675, \ldots]$.

Consider the situation now where $g_0 \neq 0$. This complicates the procedure somewhat. In this case the output of the linear portion $x(t)$ depends instantaneously upon its input $y(t)$. Thus the input of the nonlinear element $z(t)$ depends instantaneously upon its output, and the system response may not be determined by the solution of linear algebraic equations. The general equation for z_n is

$$z_n + \frac{\tau}{2} g_0 \phi_n = k - \tau\left(g_1 \phi_{n-1} + g_2 \phi_{n-2} + \cdots + g_n \frac{\phi_0}{2}\right)$$

which may be written

$$z_1 + \frac{\tau}{2} g_0 \phi_1 = k_1 - \tau\left(\frac{g_1 \phi_0}{2}\right) = k_1 - \Sigma_1{}^*$$

$$z_2 + \frac{\tau}{2} g_0 \phi_2 = k_2 - \tau\left(g_1 \phi_1 + \frac{g_2 \phi_0}{2}\right) = k_2 - \Sigma_2{}^*$$

$$\vdots$$

$$z_n + \frac{\tau}{2} g_0 \phi_n = k_n - \tau\left(g_1 \phi_{n-1} + \cdots + \frac{g_n \phi_0}{2}\right) = k_n - \Sigma_n{}^* \qquad (5.10)$$

Thus

$$z_1 - (k_1 - \Sigma_1^*) = \frac{\tau}{2} g_0 \phi_1$$

$$z_2 - (k_2 - \Sigma_2^*) = \frac{\tau}{2} g_0 \phi_2$$

$$\vdots$$

$$z_n - (k_n - \Sigma_n^*) = \frac{\tau}{2} g_0 \phi_n$$

Define

$$\varphi_A(z) = \frac{\tau}{2} g_0 \phi(z)$$

$$\varphi_B(z) = (k_n - \Sigma_n^*) - z$$

Given $\phi(z)$, τ and g_0, we may plot $\varphi_A(z)$ as in Fig. 5.31. When $k_n - \Sigma_n^*$ has been computed in the table, we may construct $\varphi_B(z)$ on Fig. 5.31. The point of intersection $\varphi_A(z) = \varphi_B(z)$ corresponds to $z = z_n$. An outline of the procedure is as follows:

1. Determine

$$S(k) = [k_0, k_1, k_2, \ldots]$$
$$S(g) = [g_0, g_1, g_2, \ldots]$$

2. Plot

$$\varphi_A(z) = \frac{\tau}{2} g_0 \phi(z)$$

3. Determine

$$k_1 - \Sigma_1^* = k_1 - \frac{\tau}{2} g_0 \phi(z_0)$$

4. Plot the line

$$\varphi_B(z) = (k_1 - \Sigma_1^*) - z$$

5. Determine z_1 such that $\varphi_A(z_1) = \varphi_B(z_1)$
6. Determine from the table:

$$(k_2 - \Sigma_2^*)$$

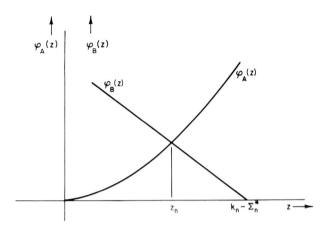

FIG. **5.31**   Graphical solution.

7. Plot the line

$$\varphi_B(z) = (k_2 - \Sigma_2{}^*) - z$$

and so forth.

It is also frequently convenient to plot z_n and ϕ_n versus $k_n - \Sigma_n{}^*$.
The solution of the equation

$$\frac{\tau}{2} g_0 \phi(z_n) = k_n - \Sigma_n{}^* - z_n$$

may be solved on a computer during the process of the tabulation by iteration.
However, it is usually more convenient to tabulate in the computer memory
not only the function $\phi(z)$ for the range of interest of z, but also the function

$$B(z) = \frac{\tau}{2} g_0 \phi(z) + z$$

say, for the points $z^0, z^1, z^2, \ldots, z^i, z^{i+1}, \ldots$, which is easily constructed as
in Fig. 5.32.

After computation of $(k_n - \Sigma_n{}^*)$, we desire a value of z_n such that

$$B(z) = k_n - \Sigma_n{}^*$$

First we determine i such that

$$B^i \le k_n - \Sigma_n{}^* < B^{i+1}$$

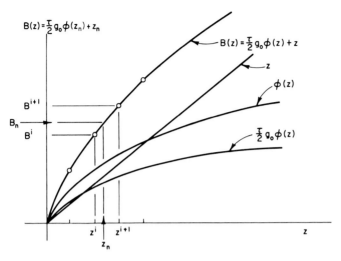

FIG. **5.32** Determination of $B(z)$ for a nonlinear system.

and the related values z^i and z^{i+1}. Then, by linear interpolation, we have

$$z_n = z^i + (z^{i+1} - z^i) \frac{(k_n - \sum_n^*) - B^i}{B^{i+1} - B^i}$$

It is, of course, convenient and reasonable to choose the internal $(z^{i+1} - z^i)$ constant over the range of z. If the inverse of $B(z)$ is not single-valued, special care must be taken to insure the correct value of z, depending upon the characteristics of $\phi(z)$.

EXAMPLE 5.12

Consider the system in Fig. 5.33, where

$$k(t) = u(t), \qquad g(t) = \frac{1}{T} u(t), \qquad T = 5, \qquad \text{and} \qquad \tau = 1$$

$$S(k) = [1, 1, 1, \ldots], \qquad S(g) = [0.2, 0.2, 0.2, \ldots]$$

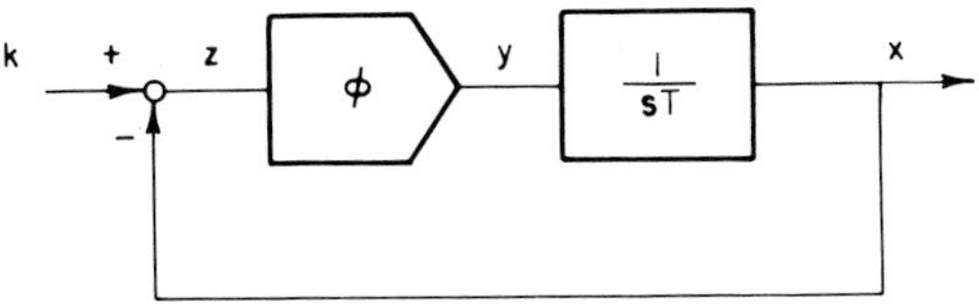

FIG. **5.33** Example 5.12, nonlinear system.

Consider the case where $\phi(z) = z$ (linear). In Fig. 5.34 we plot

$$\varphi_A(z) = \frac{\tau}{2}g_0 z = 0.1z \qquad \text{(curve 1)}$$

$$k_1 - \Sigma_1{}^* = k_1 - \frac{\tau}{2}g_1\phi(z_0) = 1 - \left(\frac{0.2}{2}\right)(1.1) = 0.89$$

and

$$\varphi_B(z) = (k_1 - \Sigma_1{}^*) - z = 0.89 - z$$

is plotted as curve 2. The intersection of curves 1 and 2 (point A) give $z_1 = 0.818$. Of course, for this case, z_1 may be calculated exactly:

$$x_1 = k_1 - z_1 = 1 - 0.818 = 0.182$$

This process is continued in tabular form as follows:

k_n	z_n	$x_n = k_n - z_n$	$y_n = \phi(z_n)$	0.2	0.2	0.2	0.2	0.2	0.2	0.2	0.2	0.2
1	1.000	0	1	0.1	0.1	0.1	0.1	0.1	0.1	0.1	0.1	0.1
				0.1								
1	0.818	0.182	0.818		0.1636	0.1636	0.1636	0.1636	0.1636	0.1636	0.1636	0.1636
					0.2636							
1	0.669	0.331	0.669			0.1338	0.1338	0.1338	0.1338	0.1338	0.1338	0.1338
						0.3974						
1	0.548	0.452	0.598				0.1096	0.1096	0.1096	0.1096	0.1096	0.1096
							0.5070					
1	0.447	0.553	0.447					0.0894	0.0894	0.0894	0.0894	0.0894
								0.5964				
1	0.368	0.632	0.368						0.0736	0.0736	0.0736	0.0736
									0.6700			
1	0.3	0.7	0.3							0.06	0.06	0.06
										0.7300		
1	0.246	0.754	0.246								0.0592	0.0592
											0.7892	
1	0.2	0.80	0.2									0.04
												0.8292
1	0.155	0.845	...									

Thus

$$S(X) = [0, 0.182, 0.331, 0.452, 0.533, 0.632, 0.700, 0.754, 0.800, 0.845, \ldots]$$

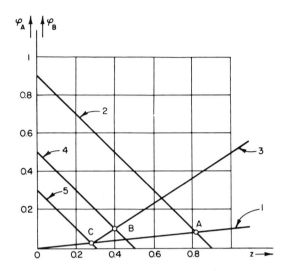

FIG. **5.34** $\varphi_A(z)$ and $\varphi_B(z)$.

This sequence is plotted as curve 1 in Fig. 5.36. This is the identical response found for this (linear) system in Chapter 4.

Suppose now that $\phi(z)$ is given by curve 3 in Fig. 5.33. Curve 3 represents $\varphi_A(z)$ and

$$\varphi_A(z) = \frac{\tau}{2} g_0 \phi(z) = 0.1\phi(z)$$

$$S(k) = [1, 1, 1, \dots], \qquad S(g) = [0.2, 0.2, 0.2, \dots]$$
$$x_0 = 0, \qquad z_0 = k_0 - x_0 = 1$$

$$\varphi_A(z_0) = \varphi_A(1) = 0.5 = \frac{\tau}{2} g_0 \phi(z_0) = 0.1\phi(z_0)$$

where

$$\phi(z_0) = \frac{0.5}{0.1} = 5$$

and

$$k_1 - \Sigma_1{}^* = k_1 - \frac{\tau}{2} g_0 \phi(z_0) = 1 - \left(\frac{0.2}{2}\right)5 = 0.5$$

Thus $\varphi_B(z)$ is the straight line shown by curve 4 in Fig. 5.33. It crosses curve 3 ($\varphi_A(z)$) at point B, corresponding to $z_1 = 0.4$. It follows that

$$x_1 = k_1 - z_1 = 1 - 0.4 = 0.6, \qquad \phi_1 = \phi(z_1) = 0.972$$

Multiplying each term of $\tau S(g)$ by this value and entering it in the top row of the following table (p. 187), we have

$$\Sigma_2{}^* = \tau g_1 \phi(z_1) + \frac{\tau g_2 \phi(z_0)}{2} = (0.2 \times 1) + \left(\frac{0.2 \times 5}{2}\right) = 0.7$$

$$k_2 - \Sigma_2{}^* = 1 - 0.7 = 0.3$$

We plot a new $\varphi_B(z)$, which intersects φ_A at point c in Fig. 5.34. Thus

$$z_2 = 0.278, \qquad \phi(z_2) = 0.278$$
$$x_2 = k_2 - z_2 = 1 - 0.278 = 0.722$$

The details of the calculation are given in the accompanying tabulation to obtain

$$S(X) = [0, 0.6, 0.722, 0.772, 0.814, 0.848, 0.875, 0.898, 0.916,$$
$$0.933, \ldots]$$

The calculation of B_n is also shown on the tabulation as

$$B_n = k_n - \Sigma_n{}^*$$

which eliminates the need to evaluate φ_B at each stage of the calculation. However, we must plot $B(z)$. This is presented in Fig. 5.35.

Starting from the initial value $x_0 = 0$, we have only to take

$$x_0 = 0, \qquad z_0 = k_0 - x_0 = 1, \qquad y_0 = \phi_0 = 5$$

$$B_1 = k_1 - \tau\left(\frac{g_1 \phi_0}{2}\right) = 0.5$$

and from Fig. 5.35,

$$\phi_1 = y_1 = 0.972 \qquad \text{and} \qquad x_1 = k_1 - z_1 = 0.6$$

which eliminates the necessity of plotting $\varphi_B(z)$ for each n.

This result is shown by curve 2 of Fig. 5.36. It can be seen that the controlled variable quickly approaches its final value. The nonlinear element acts as a variable gain, having high gain for large values of z (error) and becoming smaller for small z. In this case the step response (rise time) is improved by the introduction of the nonlinear element.

EXAMPLE 5.13

Consider the system shown in Fig. 5.37.

k_n	z_n	$x_n=k_0-z_n$	$y_n=\phi(z_n)$	0.2	0.2	0.2	0.2	0.2	0.2	0.2	0.2	0.2
1	1.0	0	5.0	0.5	0.5	0.5	0.5	0.5	0.5	0.5	0.5	0.5
1	0.4	0.6	0.972	0.5	0.194	0.194	0.194	0.194	0.194	0.194	0.194	0.194
1	0.278	0.722	0.278	$B_1=1-0.5$ $=0.5$	0.694	0.056	0.056	0.056	0.056	0.056	0.056	0.056
1	0.228	0.772	0.228		$B_2=1-0.694$ $=0.306$	0.750	0.046	0.046	0.046	0.046	0.056	0.046
1	0.186	0.814	0.186			$B_3=1-0.750$ $=0.250$	0.796	0.037	0.037	0.037	0.037	0.037
1	0.152	0.848	0.152				$B_4=1-0.796$ $=0.204$	0.833	0.030	0.030	0.030	0.030
1	0.125	0.875	0.125					$B_5=1-0.833$ $=0.167$	0.863	0.025	0.025	0.025
1	0.102	0.898	0.102						$B_6=1-0.863$ $=0.137$	0.888	0.020	0.020
1	0.084	0.916	0.084							$B_7=1-0.888$ $=0.112$	0.908	0.018
1	0.067	0.933	...								$B_8=1-0.908$ $=0.092$	0.926
												$B_9=1-0.920$ $=0.074$

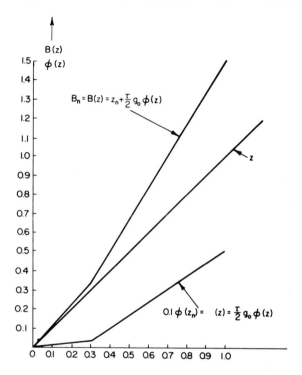

FIG. **5.35** Example of nonlinear system analysis.

For the functions $y = \phi(z)$ shown in Fig. 5.38,

$$g(t) = 2(1 - e^{-t})u(t)$$

Note that $g_0 = 0$.

It is desired to determine the response to the input

$$k(t) = 10u(t)$$

We construct the table for $g_0 = 0$ and substitute for $\phi(z)$ the nonlinearity relationships

$$\phi_a(z) = \operatorname{sgn} z \qquad\qquad\qquad\text{(Fig. 5.38(a))}$$

$$\phi_b(z) = \begin{cases} z & \text{for } |z| < 1 \\ \operatorname{sgn} z & \text{for } |z| \geq 1 \end{cases} \qquad \text{(Fig. 5.38(b))}$$

$$\phi_c(z) = \begin{cases} 0 & \text{for } |z| < 1 \\ \operatorname{sgn} z & \text{for } |z| \geq 1 \end{cases} \qquad \text{(Fig. 5.38(c))}$$

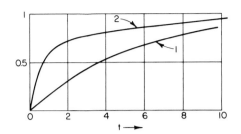

FIG. **5.36** Step response of a feedback system without (1) and with (2) nonlinear element.

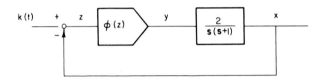

FIG. **5.37** System containing nonlinear element.

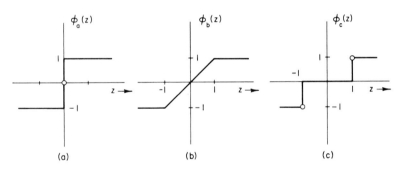

FIG. **5.38** Nonlinear characteristics.

The details of the table (programmed on a digital computer) are left as an exercise for the reader. The procedure follows Example 5.1. The results of this computation are presented in Figs. 5.39 through 5.41. Both the output $S(x)$ and the output of the nonlinear element, $y(t)$, are presented.

The methods for the determination of the response of nonlinear control systems may be adapted to design nonlinear control elements to obtain a desired output response. Given the system characteristics, input, and desired output, a nonlinear feedback characteristic may be determined by the inverse algorithm. See Problems 5.12 and 5.13 (Appendix).

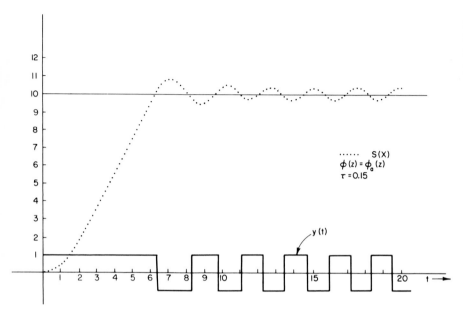

FIG. **5.39** Example 5.13.

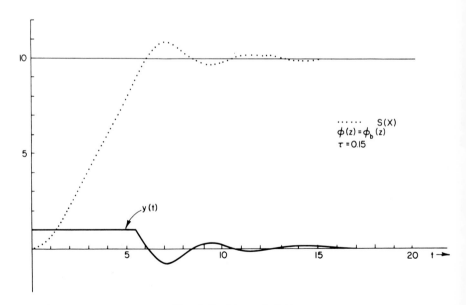

FIG. **5.40** Example 5.13.

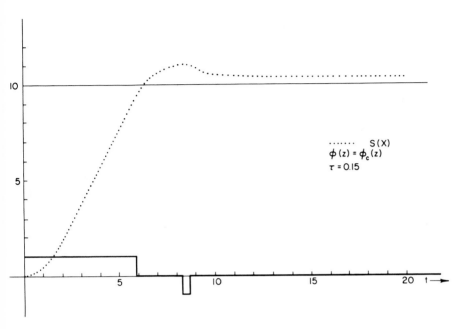

FIG. **5.41** Example 5.13.

5.6 CONCLUSIONS

Impulse analysis is a tool that is useful for the study of the dynamic behavior of systems, particularly when this behavior cannot be characterized by analytical equations, but can be determined only by measurement of the input and output variables of the system. Experience has shown that this method works well and is appropriate for use on digital computers. It is not an exact method, for its accuracy is a function of the system equations, the technique employed, the interval size, and the number of significant digits carried in the calculations. We have seen that an increase in the accuracy may be obtained by reducing the interval size at a cost of increased computation time. An optimum choice of these parameters must be found consistent with the required accuracy.

In many cases the apparent rigor of the "exact solution" is affected by the simplifications necessary to formulate the problem into equations, and in many cases engineers prefer a numerical approximation such as impulse analysis. Frequently the exactness of the "exact solution" hides inaccuracies due to the necessary simplifications, or is so unduly complicated that the method does not derive great benefit.

Many aspects of this method require further study and the authors would like to take this opportunity to suggest a few areas as follows:

1. Evaluation of the stability of the deconvolution operation
2. Accuracy of the different operators: integration, differentiation, convolution, deconvolution, solution of differential equations, and extensions of applications to nonlinear and time-varying systems
3. Applications to stochastic, multivariable nonlinear systems
4. Accuracy and stability consideration of variable-sampling interval

The authors' aim was to present the basic principles of impulse analysis and describe some of the problems involved with this method. They hope that this work serves as an introduction to and inspiration for further study in the area by both applied mathematicians and engineers.

References

1. Adams, R. K., Digital computer analysis of closed loop system using the number series approach, *IEEE Trans*. Part II (January 1962).
2. Bellman, R., and Cooke, K., "Differential-Difference Equations." Academic Press, New York, 1963.
3. Blackman, R. B., and Tukey, J. W., "The Measurement of Power Spectra." Dover New York, 1958.
4. Boxer, R., and Thaler, S. A simplified method of solving linear and nonlinear system, *Proc. IRE*, **44**, 89–101 (1956).
5. Bracewell, R., "The Fourier Transform and Its Applications." McGraw-Hill, New York, 1965.
6. Cruikshank, A. J. O., A note on time series and the use of jump functions in approximate analysis, *Proc. IEE*, **102** Part C, 81–87 (1955).
7. Cuénod, M., "Etude des phénomènes transitoires à l'aide de suites de temps," *Bull. Technique Suisse Romande* **16** (1949).
8. Cuénod, M., "Méthode de Calcul à l'aide de suites de temps." Imprimarie La Concorde, Lausanne, 1955.
9. Cuénod, M., "Contribution to the Study of Floods. Calculation Using a Series Method of the Dynamic Relation between Rainfall and River Flow." La Houille Blanche Sept. 1956 No. 3.
10. Cuénod, M., Principe de l'analyse impulsionnelle et de son application à la théorie des servomécanismes, L'Onde Electrique août-sept. 1956 p. 365–366.
11. Cuénod, M., Etude de la réponse d'un système linéaire au moyen de l'analyse impulsionnelle, *Rev. gén. d'élect.* **65**, 118–126 (1956).
12. Durling, A., and Rosko, J., Discrete integration with bounded rate of error accumulation, *IEEE Trans. Automatic Control* [4] **AC-11** (1966).
13. Enriques, F., "Les Concepts Fondamentaux de la Science."
14. Erdelyi, A., "Operational Calculus and Generalized Functions." Holt, New York, 1962.
15. Friedland, B., A technique for the analysis of time varying sampled data systems, *AIEE Trans.* **75**, Part 2 407–414 (1957).
16. Halijak, C. A., Digital Approximation of the Solutions of Differential Equations Using Trapezoidal Convolution. Report No. ITM-64, System Division of Bendix Corporation, Ann Arbor, Michigan, August, 1960.

17. Horowitz, I. M., "Synthesis of Feedback Systems" (Chap. 11). Academic Press, New York, 1963.
18. Jury, E. I., "Sampled Data Control Systems." Wiley, New York, 1958.
19. Jury, E. I., "Theory and Applications of the z-transform Methods." Wiley, New York, 1964.
20. Kaplan, W., "Operational Method for Linear Systems." Addison-Wesley, Reading, Massachusetts, 1962.
21. Laible, T., Essais de réglage de tension à la centrale de Lünersee, *Bull. Oerlikon*, **339**, 30–35 (1960).
22. Lepage, W. R., "Complex Variables and Laplace Transforms for Engineers." McGraw-Hill, New York, 1960.
23. Madwed, A., Number Series Methods of Solving Linear and Non-linear Differential Equations, Report No. 6445-T-26, Instrumentation Lab. MIT., 1950.
24. Mikusinski, J., "Operational Calculus." Pergamon, Oxford, 1959.
25. Naslin, P., "Les régimes variables dans les systèmes linéaires et nonlineaires, (Chapters 3 and 7). Dunod, Paris, 1962.
26. Naumov, B., Approximated method for calculating the time response in linear, time varying and nonlinear automatic control systems. *J. Basic Eng. Trans. ASME* **83**, Series D 109–118 (1961).
27. Papoulis, A., "The Fourier Transform and Its Applications." McGraw-Hill, New York, 1962.
28. T. Ch. Gille, P. Decaulne, and M. Pélegrin, "Méthodes modernes d'étude des systèmes asservis." Dunod, Paris, 1960.
29. Pierre, D. A., A tabular algorithm for z-transform inversion, *Control Eng.* **74**, 110–111 (1963).
30. Powell, H. M., A Number Series Method for Digital Computer Solution of Differential Equations, MS thesis, University of Tennessee, Knoxville, Tennessee, 1958.
31. Ragazzini, J. R., and A. R. Bergen, A mathematical technique for the analysis of linear system, *Proc. IRE* **42**, 1645–1651 (1954).
32. Ragazzini, J. R., and Franklin, G. E., "Sampled Data Control Systems." McGraw-Hill, New York, 1958.
33. Richtmyer, R. D., "Difference Methods for Initial-Value Problems." Wiley, (Interscience), New York, 1957.
34. Rickard, D., A Method for Selecting the Basic Independent Variable Increment in a Number Series Calculation, (MS thesis, University of Tennessee, Knoxville, Tennessee, 1958.
35. Ronveaux, A., Integrations approchées des équations et des systèmes d'équations différentielles linéaires au moyen d'opérateurs numériques, Thèse de doctorat, Faculté des Sciences, Université de Montreal, Montreal, P.Q., 1961).
36. Rosko, J. S., Spectral error of higher order z-integrators, *Proc. IEEE* [5] **54**, 805–806 (1966).
37. Rosko, J., Design of Time Optimal Digitally Simulated Systems, Ph.D. dissertation, University of Florida, Gainesville, Florida, 1966.
38. Rosko, J., and Durling, A., Optimal simulation of linear systems, *Proc. Natl. Electronics Conf., Chicago, Illinois.* **XXIII**, 170–174 (1967).
39. Stiefel, E., Introduction à la théorie des distributions pour l'étude des réglages linéaires, *Bull. Techn. de la Suisse Romande* **18** 289–295 (1957).

40. Stout, T. M., Step by step method for transient analysis of feedback systems with one nonlinear element, *AIEE Trans.* **75**, 11 (1956), 378–390 (1957).
41. Tou, J. T., "Digital and Sampled-Data Control Systems." McGraw-Hill, New York, 1955.
42. Truxal, J. G., Numerical analysis for network design, *Trans. IRE* **CT-1**, 49–60 (1954).
43. Truxal, J. G., "Control System Synthesis," (Chapters 1–6, 9). McGraw-Hill, New York, 1955.
44. Tschanner, J., "Einführung in die Theorie der Abtast Systeme." Oldenburg, Munich, 1960.
45. Tustin, A., A method of analyzing the behavior of linear systems in terms of time series. Also: A method of analyzing the effects of certain kinds of nonlinearity in closed-cycle control systems. *Proc. Con. Automatic Regulators Servomechanisms* **94** Part II A, 130 ff. (1947).
46. Unbehauen, H., Identification of the system parameters and development of the mathematical model of a control system by means of the measured time response, *Proc. IFAC Tokyo Symp. Systems Eng. Control System Design* (1965).
47. Wagner, K. W., Ed., "Operatoren Rechnung." Barth, Leipzig, 1940.
48. Weaver, C. W., The Analysis and Design of Linear Closed Loop Control Systems by Means of Number Series, Ph.D. thesis, University of Wisconsin, Madison, Wisconsin, 1955.

Table of Main Formulas

(1.1)   Functional approximation with a sequence

$$S(F) = [f_0, f_1, f_2, \ldots, f_n, \ldots]$$

with $f_n = f(n\tau)$.

(1.2)   Intermediate value sequence

$$S_v(F) = [f_0^v, f_1^v, \ldots, f_n^v, \ldots]$$

where $f_n^v = f((2n + 1)/2\tau) = f((n + \frac{1}{2})\tau)$.

(1.3)   Intermediate interpolating sequence

$$S_i(F) = [f_0^i, f_1^i, \ldots, f_n^i, \ldots]$$

where $f_n^i = (f(n\tau) + f((n + 1)\tau))/2$.

(1.4)   Intermediate area sequence

$$S_a(F) = [f_0^a, f_1^a, \ldots, f_n^a, \ldots]$$

where $f_n^a = 1/\tau \int_{n\tau}^{(n + 1)\tau} f(t)\, dt$.

(1.5)   Intermediate area with quadratic parabola interpolation

$$f_k^a = \frac{\tau}{6} [f(k\tau) + 4f(k + \frac{1}{2})\tau + f((k + 1)\tau)]$$

(1.6) $f_k^a = \frac{1}{3}[2f_k^v + f_k^i]$

(1.7)   Step sequence

$$S_e(F) = [f_0^e, f_1^e, \ldots, f_n^e]$$

where $f_n^e = f_n - \sum_{i=0}^{n-1} f_i^e = f_n - f_{n-1}.$

(1.8)   Ramp sequence

$$S_r(F) = [f_0^r, f_1^r, \ldots, f_n^r, \ldots]$$

where $f_n^r = f_n + 2\sum_{k=1}^{n-1} (-1)^k f_k + (-1)^n f_0.$

(1.9)   Definition of the E operator

$$Ef(t) = f(t - \tau)$$

(1.10)   Definition of the z operator

$$zf(t) = f(t + \tau)$$

(1.11) E Transform

$$F(E) = \tau \sum_{n=0}^{\infty} f_n E^n$$

(1.12) z Transform

$$F(z) = \tau \sum_{n=0}^{\infty} f_n z^{-n}$$

(2.1)   Convolution

$$b(k\tau) = \tau \sum_{n=0}^{k} a_n g(k\tau - n\tau) = \tau \sum_{n=0}^{k} a_n g_{k-n}$$

where $a(t)$ is the input, $b(t)$ the output, and $g(t)$ the impulse response of the transfer element.

(2.2)   Duhamel integral

$$b(t) = \int_0^t a(x)g(t - x) \, dx$$

(2.3)   Convolution with the E transform

$$B(E) = \tau^2 \sum_{n=0}^{\infty} \sum_{m=0}^{\infty} a_m g_n E^{n+m}$$

(2.4)   Convolution with the trapezoidal integration

$$S(B) = S(A) * S(G) + \frac{a_0 g_0}{4}$$

(2.5)   Convolution with intermediate area sequence

$$S(B) = S_a(A) * S_a(G)$$

(2.6)   Convolution with intermediate value sequence

$$S(B) = S_v(A) * S_v(G)D(-1)$$

where $D(-1)$ is the shift of each term of one position forward.

(2.7)   Convolution with the step response

$$b(t) = \int_0^\infty \underline{a'(\tau)}\gamma(t - \tau) \, d\tau = \underline{a'(t)} * \gamma(t)$$

with $\underline{a'(t)}$ = generalized derivation of $a(t)$.

(2.8)   Convolution with the step sequence

$$S(B) = S_e(A) * S(\gamma)$$

(2.9)   Integrating operator

$$\frac{1}{s^n} = \lim_{a \to 0} \frac{\tau(-1)^{n-1}}{(n-1)!} \left[\frac{\partial^{n-1}}{\partial a^{n-1}} \left(\frac{z}{z - e^{-a\tau}} \right) \right]$$

(2.10)   Convolution with discontinuous functions

$$f(t) * g(t) = f_2(t) * g(t) + f(0^+)\gamma(t)$$

(2.11)   Deconvolution

$$g_n = \frac{1}{a_0}\left(b_n - \sum_{k-1}^n a_k g_{n-k} \right)$$

(2.12)   Initial value theorem

$$g_0 = g(0) = \lim_{s \to \infty} \frac{2b_1}{\tau a_1} = \frac{2b_1}{\tau a_1}$$

(2.13)   First integration

$$S(I_1) = \tau S(F) * \left[\frac{1}{2}, 1, 1, \ldots, 1, \ldots \right] - \frac{\tau}{2}f_0[1, 1, \ldots, 1, \ldots]$$

(2.14) kth integration

$$S(I_k) = S(F) * \tau^k \left[\frac{1}{2}, 1, 1, \ldots, 1, \ldots\right]^{-k}$$

$$- \frac{\tau^{-k}}{2} f_0 [1, 1, \ldots, 1, \ldots] * \left[\frac{1}{2}, 1, 1, \ldots\right]^{k-1}$$

where $I_k = \int_0^t \cdots \int_0^t f(t)(dt)^k$

(2.15)   Integration with the use of the intermediate area sequence

$$S(I_k) = \frac{\tau^k}{k!} S_e(F) * [0, 1^k, 2^k, 3^k, \ldots]$$

(2.61)   Differentiation

$$S\left(\frac{df}{dt}\right) = \frac{1}{2\tau} [S(F) * [1, 0, -1]D(+1)]$$

(2.17)   Differentiation with the use of the step sequence

$$S\left(\frac{df}{dt}\right) = \frac{1}{\tau} S_v(F) * [1, -1]$$

(3.1)   Linear differential equation of first order

$$S(X) = \frac{\tau S(F) * [\frac{1}{2}, 1, 1, \ldots, 1, \ldots] + ((a + b\tau/2)x_0 - \tau f_0)/2[1, 1, \ldots, 1, \ldots]}{[a] + b\tau[\frac{1}{2}, 1, 1, \ldots, 1, \ldots]}$$

(3.2)   Linear differential equation of first order, with matrix notation

$$S(X) = [S(F)\mathbf{B} + ax_0[1, 1, \ldots, 1, \ldots]]\mathbf{C}^{-1}$$

where $\mathbf{C} = [[\diagdown^a] + b\mathbf{B}]$

(3.3)   Differential equation with time varying coefficients with matrix notation

$$S(X) = [S(F)\mathbf{B} + a_0 x_0 [1, 1, \ldots, 1, \ldots]]\mathbf{C}^{-1}$$

where $\mathbf{C} = [\diagdown^a] + [\diagdown^{b-a}]\mathbf{B}$

(3.4)   Differential equation with time varying coefficients in sequence notation

$$y_n = \frac{c_n - \Sigma_n}{\alpha_n}$$

where $\Sigma_n = \tau[(a_0 y_0/2) + a_1 y_1 + \cdots + a_{n-1} y_{n-1}]$

and $\alpha_n = 1 + \tau a_n/2$.

(3.5)   Second order differential equation in sequence notation

$$y_n = \frac{c_n + \Sigma_n}{\alpha_n}$$

where:

$$\Sigma_n = \tau \left(\sum_{k=1}^{n-1} (v_k - k\tau b_k) y_k \right) + \frac{\tau}{2} (v_0 - n\tau b_0) y_0$$

$$\alpha_n = u_n - \frac{\tau v_n}{2} + n\tau^2 b_n$$

$$u(t) = 1 + a(t)$$

$$\dot{a}(t) = v(t)$$

$$c(t) = (1 + a_0) y_0 + \dot{y}_0 t + \int_0^i \int_0^t f(t)(dt)^2$$

(3.6)   Nonlinear differential equation

$$\frac{y_n}{B_n} = \frac{1}{1 + \dfrac{\tau}{2} a(y_n)}$$

where $B_n = c_n - \tau \Sigma_n$ and $\Sigma_n = \sum_{k=1}^{n-1} y_k a(y_k) - (y_0/2) a(y_0)$

(4.20)   Total accumulated error

$$E_{n+1} = E_n + \tau(f_n - g_n) - \frac{\tau^2}{2} y''(\theta_n)$$

where $n\tau \le \theta_n \le (n + 1)\tau.$

(5.1)   System response to a deterministic input with the use of the impulse response

$$S(C) = \frac{\tau[S_i(k) * S_i(g_k)] D(-1)}{[1] + \tau S_i(g_r)}$$

(5.2)   System response to a deterministic input with the use of the step response

$$S(C) = \frac{S_i(k) * S(\gamma_k)}{[1, 1, \ldots, 1, \ldots] + S_i(\gamma_r)}$$

(5.3)   System response to stochastic inputs

$$R_{yy}(\theta) = \int_0^\infty R_{xx}(u - \theta)R_g(u)\,du$$

$$+ \int_0^\infty R_{xx}(u + \theta)R_g(u)\,du$$

Meansquare value of the output of a system with stochastic input

$$\bar{y}_2 = R_{yy}(0) = \tau\left[rx_0rg_0 + \sum_{n=1}^\infty rx_nrg_n\right]$$

$$= \tau\left[rx_0rg_0 + 2\sum_{n=1}^N rx_nrg_n\right]$$

(5.4)   Multivariable system identification

$$S(G_{mx}) = \frac{\begin{vmatrix} S(x_1) & S(n_1) & \cdots & S(k_1) \\ S(x_2) & S(n_2) & \cdots & S(k_2) \\ & \vdots & & \\ S(x_k) & S(n_k) & \cdots & S(k_k) \end{vmatrix}}{\begin{vmatrix} S(m_1) & S(n_1) & \cdots & S(k_1) \\ S(m_2) & S(n_2) & \cdots & S(k_2) \\ & \vdots & & \\ S(m_k) & S(n_k) & \cdots & S(k_k) \end{vmatrix}}$$

(5.5)   Multivariable control system response to deterministic input

$$S(x) = \frac{\begin{vmatrix} -[S(m) * S(G_{mx}) + S(n) * S(G_{nx})] & S(G_{yx}) \cdots \\ -[S(m) * S(G_{my}) + S(n) * S(G_{ny})] & S(G_{yy}) - [1] \cdots \\ \vdots & \vdots \end{vmatrix}}{\begin{vmatrix} S(G_{xx}) - [1] & S(G_{yx}) \cdots \\ S(G_{xy}) & S(G_{yy}) - [1] \cdots \\ \vdots & \vdots \end{vmatrix}}$$

(5.6)   System identification through deconvolution

$$S(\gamma) = \frac{S(Y) * [1, 1, \ldots, 1, \ldots]}{S_i(X)} = \frac{S(Y)}{S_i(X) * [1, -1]}$$

(5.7)   Frequency response

$$H(j\omega) = \frac{1}{j\omega}\int_0^\infty e^{-j\omega t}\dot{\gamma}(t)\,dt + \gamma(0) + \frac{\dot{\gamma}(0)}{j\omega}$$

(5.8)   System identification of processes with random input

$$S(G) = \frac{1}{\tau} \frac{S(Z)}{S(X)} = \frac{1}{\tau} \frac{S(R_{xy}(\theta))}{S(R_{xx}(\theta))}$$

(5.9)   Response of a nonlinear system with

$$z_n = k_n - \tau \left[g_1 \phi_{n-1} + g_2 \phi_{n-2} + \cdots + \frac{g_n \phi_0}{2} \right]$$

where $\phi_n = \phi(z(n\tau))$ = characteristic of the nonlinear element.

(5.10)   Response of a nonlinear system with

$$z_n + \frac{\tau}{2} g_0 \phi_n = k_n - \tau \left(g_1 \phi_{n-1} + \cdots + g_n \frac{\phi_0}{2} \right) = k_n - \Sigma_n{}^*$$

where $\Sigma_n{}^* = \tau(g_1 \phi_{n-1} + \cdots + g_n \phi_0 / 2)$.

APPENDIX Problems

Chapter 2

P2.1 Perform the convolution presented as Example 2.2 for $\tau = \frac{1}{2}$.

$$g(t) = \tfrac{1}{2}e^{-t/2}u(t), \qquad R_{xx}(\theta) = e^{-|\theta|}$$

P2.2 Consider a system with transfer function

$$G(s) = \frac{1}{(2s + 1)(2.5s + 1)}$$

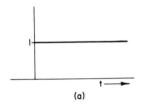

(a)

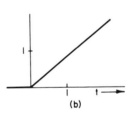

(b)

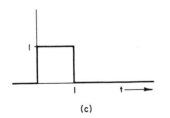

(c)

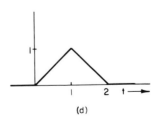

(d)

FIG. **P2.2**

Determine the system response (by numerical convolution) to the inputs given in Fig. P2.2. Compare the results with the exact solution for various values of the independent variable increment.

P2.3   Perform the convolution $f(t) * g(t)$ by reducing $f(t)$ and $g(t)$ to sequences of impulses, convoluting and then integrating. Repeat, using the z-transform notation presented in Sec. 2.23.

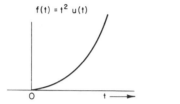

Fig. **P2.3**

P2.4   Repeat Problem 2.3 for $g(t)$ as given in Fig. P2.4.

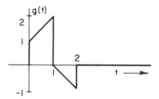

Fig. **P2.4**

P2.5   The measured step response of a (assumed) linear system is given in sequence notation as (for $\tau = 1$ ms)

$$S(G) = [10.0, 11.8, 12.6, 12.5, 11.5, 10.0, 8.0, 6.3,$$
$$5.2, 4.4, 3.8, 3.5, 3.2, 3.1, 3.0, 3.0, 3.0, \ldots]$$

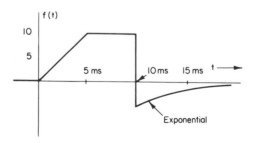

Fig. **P2.5**

Determine the response due to the input shown in Fig. P2.5.
Sketch the step response, input, and output.

P2.6 The deconvolution of the sequences $S(y)$ and $S(x)$ yield the result $S(G) = S(y)/S(x)$. Assume that for small t, $x(t)$ and $y(t)$ may be approximated by parabolas passing through the points $(0, x_1, x_2)$ and $(0, y_1, y_2)$ as shown in Fig. P2.6.

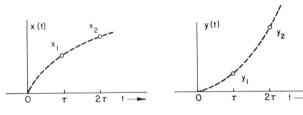

FIG. **P2.6**

Show (on this assumption) that the initial term of the deconvolution for the step response $(S(y))$ and impulse response $(S(G))$ are

$$g_0 = \frac{y_2 - 2y_1}{4\tau(4x_1 - x_2)} \quad \text{for } 4y_1 = y_2 \quad \text{and} \quad 4x_1 \neq x_2$$

$$\gamma_0 = \frac{4y_1 - y_2}{4x_1 - x_2} \quad \text{for } 4x_1 \quad \neq x_2$$

$$= \frac{y_2 - 2y_1}{x_2 - 2x_1} \quad \text{for } 4x_1 \quad = x_2$$

P2.7 Verify the entries in Table 2.11.

P2.8 Given

$$S(F) = [0.6, 0.8, 1, 1, 1, 0.8, 0.6, 0.4, 0.2]$$

For $\tau = 1$, evaluate $S(G_1)$ by use of

1. Exact solution
2. $\tau S(F) * [1, 1, 1, \ldots] = \tau S(F) \underset{*}{*} [1, -1]$
3. $\tau S(F) * \left[\frac{1}{2}, 1, 1, \ldots\right] - \frac{\tau f_0}{2} [1, 1, 1, \ldots]$
4. $\tau S_i(F) * [1, 1, 1, \ldots]$
5. $\tau S_e(F) * [0, 1, 2, 3, \ldots]$
6. $S(F)\mathbf{B}_2$

  7. $S(F)\mathbf{B}_3$

  8. Compare your results for (1) through (7) with Table 2.11 and comment. (*Note*: For the generalized integrating operator, first separate $f(t)$ into the sum of a continuous function and a piecewise constant function.)

P2.9   For $\tau = 1$, evaluate $S(G_2)$ by use of

  1. Exact solution

  2. $\tau^2 S(F) * [1, 1, 1, \ldots]^2 = \tau^2 S(F) \,\substack{*\\*}\, [1, -1]^2 = \tau^2 S(F) \,\substack{*\\*}\, [1, 0, -1]$

  3. $\tau^2 S(F) * \left[\frac{1}{2}, 1, 1, \ldots\right]^2 - \frac{\tau^2 f_0}{2} [0.5, 1.5, 2.5, 3.5, \ldots]$

  4. $\tau S(G_1)_{\text{exact}} * [0.5, 1, 1, \ldots] - \frac{\tau g_0}{2} [1, 1, 1, \ldots]$

  5. $\frac{\tau^2}{2} S_e(F) * [0, 1, 2^2, 3^2, 4^2, \ldots]$

  6. $S(F)\mathbf{B}_2{}^2$

  7. Compare your results with Table 2.11 and comment.

P2.10   Show that the approximate second-derivative formulation

$$S(f) = \frac{1}{\tau^2} [S(F) * (1, -2, 1)]D(1)$$

has a first-term correction to yield

$$S(f) = \frac{1}{\tau^2} [S(F) * (1, -2, 1)]D(1) + \left[\frac{2f_2 - 3f_1}{\tau^2}\right]$$

P2.11   Verify the correction terms for the following sequences given in Sec. 2.5:

$$S(G) = \frac{1}{\tau} S_v(F) * [1, -1] + \frac{1}{\tau}\left[2f_0^v - \frac{1}{3}f_1^v\right]$$

$$= \frac{1}{2\tau} [S(F) * [1, 0, -1]]D(1) + \left[\frac{3f_1 - f_2}{2\tau}\right]$$

P2.12   Add appropriate correction terms to the forward and backward difference formulations of the derivative:

$$S_B(G) = \frac{1}{\tau} S(F) * [1, 1]$$

$$S_F(G) = \frac{1}{\tau} (S(F) * [1, -1])D(1)$$

Chapter 3

P3.1 Evaluate the solution of the equation

$$8\frac{dx(t)}{dt} + x(t) = u(t), \qquad x(0) = 0$$

Use the matrix formulation of trapezoidal integration and compare the results as a function of the increment size with the exact solution.

P3.2 Use the integration matrix to determine $S(x)$ for the differential equation

$$\frac{dx^2(t)}{dt^2} + 2\delta\omega_0{}^2 x(t) = \omega_0{}^2 f(t)$$

For

$$f(t) = u(t),$$
$$\delta = 0.4, \qquad x(0) = 0, \qquad \omega_0 = 1$$

Compare the resultant $S(x)$ with the exact solution:

$$x(t) = 1 - \frac{1}{\sqrt{1 - \delta^2}} e^{-\delta\omega_0 t} \sin\left(\omega_0 t + \tan^{-1}\sqrt{\frac{1 - \delta^2}{\delta^2}}\right)$$

P3.3 Repeat Problem 3.2, using the Boxer-Thaler substitution.

P3.4 Repeat Problem 3.2, using trapezoidal integration for $S(x)$ and rectangular integration for $S(F)$. Comment on the application of different integral formulations within the same equation.

P3.5 In Example 3.2 the statement is made that greater accuracy may be obtained if $\omega(x)$ is approximated by the sequence

$$S_2(\omega) = \omega_0[0, 0, 0, 0, 0.5, 1, 1, 0.5, 0, 0, 0]$$

Verify this statement by evaluating $S_2(y)$. Why is this result more accurate?

P3.6 Investigate the stability of the system shown in Example 5.3 of Section 5.1 through application of sequence notation to determine the step response. (Stable for $T_i < \alpha/2$.)

P3.7 Numerically evaluate the solution of the equation

$$10\frac{dx}{dt} + x(t - \alpha) = u(t); \qquad \{x(t) = 0\} \qquad \text{for } t < 0$$

and for $\alpha = 0, 1, 2, 4,$ and 8.

Sketch the results and compare with the exact solution:

$$x(t) = \frac{1}{100} \sum_{k=1}^{\infty} (-1)^{k-1} \frac{(t - \alpha k)^k}{k!} u[t - \alpha(k - 1)]$$

P3.8   Set up a tabular algorithm for the solution of the equation

$$\frac{dy(t)}{dt} + y(t)y(t - \theta) = f(t)$$

Solve the equation for $\theta = 1$ and $(\tau = 0.5, 1, 0.01)$.

   Answer:
   $(\tau = 0.5)$
       $S(y) = [0, 0.5, 1.0, 1.333, 1.333, 1.125, 0.938, 0.878, 0.916,$
           $0.988, 1.034, 1.04, 1.020, 0.997, \ldots]$
   $(\tau = 1)$
       $S(y) = [0, 1, 1.333, 1, 0.889, 1, 1.037, 1, 0.988, 1, 1.004, \ldots]$
   $(\tau = 0.5$, computation increment $= 0.01)$
       $S(y) = [0, 0.490, 0.990, 1.334, 1.325, 1.099, 0.921, 0.881,$
           $0.932, 1.002, 1.039, 1.035, 1.011, 0.991, 0.986,$
           $0.992, 1.000, 1.005, 1.004, 1.001, 0.999, \ldots]$

P3.9   Consider the differential equation

$$\frac{dy}{dt} + y^{3/2} = tu(t), \qquad y(0) = 0$$

a special case of the equation

$$\frac{dy}{dt} \quad a(y)y(t) = f(t)$$

and determine $y(t)$ for an increment $\tau = 0.5$.

   Answer:
       $S(y) = [0, 0.125, 0.4, 0.8, 1.17, 1.5, 1.77, 2.1, \ldots]$

Chapter 4

P4.1   Evaluate on a digital computer the derivative of the function $f(x) = 1/x$ at the points $x = 1$ and $x = 2$ by Eq. 4.1 for various increment sizes.

Determine that value of τ which yields the best trade-off between the truncation error introduced by Eq. 4.1 and the round-off error. (Decrease τ sufficiently so that the round-off errors dominate, and plot the error versus τ.)

P4.2   If the differential equation

$$\frac{dy}{dt} = Ay$$

is integrated by Simpson's rule to obtain

$$y(z) = \frac{\tau}{2}\left(\frac{z^2 + 4z + 1}{z^2 - 1}\right)F(z)$$

the general term of $S(y)$ is

$$y_{n+1} = y_{n-1} + \frac{\tau}{3}(f_{n-1} + 4f_n + f_{n-1}) + E_n$$

where E_n is the truncation error introduced at the nth step. Assume that the exact solution is $S(w)$, where $f_n = Aw_n$, $w_n = y_n + e_n$, and e_n is the total error.

Show that the total error e_n satisfies the same recurrence relation as the solution y_n.

P4.3   Write a computer program to simulate a general fourth-order linear system by the Madwed-Truxal technique. Use this program to verify the entries of Tables 4.2 and 4.3.

P4.4   Repeat Problem 4.3 for (a) Tustin, (b) Boxer-Thaler, (c) first difference, (d) Halijak, and (e) the z-transform techniques.

P4.5   Suppose a numerical calculation is carried out with increment size τ_0 and $2\tau_0$ yielding solutions that differ by E. Assume that no error occurs for $\tau = 0$ and that the error varies linearly with τ. Determine the error in the two solutions in terms of E.

P4.6   (a) Perform the Tustin substitution of Example 4.5 and evaluate the step response for $\tau = 0.1063\ 4431$.
  (b) Repeat for the "optimum" τ found in (a).

Answer 4.6(a):

Time	Response	Time	Response
0.	0.06881196	5.53707510	1.17378287
0.34606721	0.36662223	5.88314229	1.08267543
0.69213443	0.95067308	6.22920948	0.99843990
1.03820163	1.65368819	6.57527667	0.94844061
1.38426884	2.21496210	6.92134386	0.94028340
1.73033604	2.44922671	7.26741105	0.96387964
2.07640323	2.32424697	7.61347824	0.99993499
2.42247042	1.94732313	7.95954543	1.02982084
2.76853761	1.49425563	8.30561256	1.04258858
3.11460480	1.12646163	8.65167975	1.03713454
3.46067199	0.93346001	8.99774694	1.01995371
3.80673918	0.91747450	9.34381413	1.00053094
4.15280634	1.01571383	9.68988132	0.98679944
4.49887353	1.14159729	10.03594851	0.98242366
4.84494072	1.22449861	⋮	⋮
5.19100791	1.23244528		

Answer 4.6(b):

Time	Response	Time	Response
0.	0.09346141	5.59392565	1.17124020
0.39956613	0.48477352	5.99349177	1.06303345
0.79913226	1.20246832	6.39305788	0.97207525
1.19869839	1.95885803	6.79262400	0.93354531
1.59826452	2.40180537	7.19219011	0.94774023
1.99783064	2.37597984	7.59175622	0.98973812
2.39739677	1.97942773	7.99132234	1.02883203
2.79696289	1.46021993	8.39088845	1.04523149
3.19652900	1.05884591	8.79045451	1.03653622
3.59609511	0.89486079	9.19002056	1.01374483
3.99566123	0.94368728	9.58958662	0.99181895
4.39522731	1.09025458	9.8915267	0.98106861
4.79479343	1.21129152	10.38871872	0.98331970
5.19435954	1.23755911	⋮	⋮

P4.7 Repeat Example 4.7 with $A = 0.001$.
  Answer:

x	e^{-x}	$\int_0^x e^{-x}\,dx$
0.	1.00000	0.
0.00781	0.99221	0.00778
0.2343	0.97683	0.02316
0.05468	0.94678	0.05322
0.11718	0.88941	0.11060
0.17968	0.83553	0.16450
0.24218	0.78490	0.21514
0.30468	0.73735	0.26271
0.42968	0.65071	0.34947
0.55468	0.57425	0.42603
0.67969	0.50677	0.49359
0.80458	0.44722	0.55322
0.92968	0.39457	0.60584
1.05468	0.34830	0.65227
1.17968	0.39737	0.69325
1.30468	0.27125	0.72942
1.42968	0.23938	0.76133
1.55468	0.21125	0.78950
1.67968	0.18643	0.81435
1.92968	0.14519	0.85580
2.17968	0.11307	0.88809
2.42968	0.08806	0.91323
2.67968	0.06858	0.93281
2.92968	0.05341	0.94806
3.17968	0.04159	0.95994
3.67968	0.02523	0.97665
4.17968	0.01530	0.98678
4.67968	0.00928	0.99293
5.67968	0.00341	0.99927
7.67968	0.00046	1.00315
10.00000	0.00004	1.00374

Chapter 5

P5.1 Consider the system shown in Fig. P5.1. Determine, by application of the methods of Chapter 5, the step response of the system. Compare the results as a function of sample increment size with the exact response.

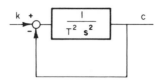

FIG. **P5.1**

P5.2 For the system shown in Fig. P5.2, determine the system step response for $T_a = 5$, 10, and 20 s. When $T_r = 2$ s, $a = 1$, and $k = 20$.

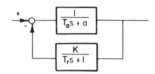

FIG. **P5.2**

Answer:

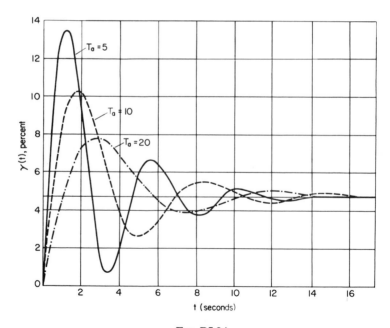

FIG. **P5.2A**

P5.3 Determine the step response sequence of the system shown in Fig. P5.3
for T_a = 5, 10, and 20 s, T_r = 2 s, k = 20, a = 1, T_p = 5 s.

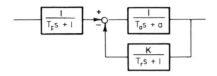

FIG. **P5.3**

Answer:

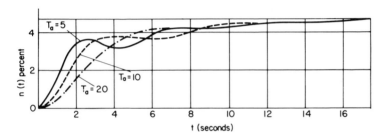

FIG. **P5.3A**

P5.4 Verify the relations given in Section 5.3.

$$S(x_1) = [Q_1 P_{12}{}^{-1} - Q_2 P_{22}{}^{-1}] \underset{*}{*} [P_{11} P_{12}{}^{-1} - P_{21} P_{22}]$$
$$S(x_2) = [Q_1 P_{11}{}^{-1} - Q_2 P_{21}{}^{-1}] \underset{*}{*} [P_{12} P_{11}{}^{-1} - P_{22} P_{21}{}^{-1}]$$

P5.5 In Sec. 5.3.2 the equations

$$S(x_1) = S(m_1) * S(G_{mx}) + S(n_1) * S(G_{nx})$$
$$S(x_2) = S(m_2) * S(G_{mx}) + S(n_2) * S(G_{nx})$$

were solved to yield

$$S(G_{mx}) = \frac{S(x_1) * S(n_2) - S(x_1) * S(n_1)}{S(m_1) * S(n_2) - S(m_2) * S(n_1)}$$

$$S(G_{nx}) = \frac{S(m_1) * S(x_2) - S(m_2) * S(x_1)}{S(m_1) * S(n_2) - S(m_2) * S(n_1)}$$

Verify that these operations are valid.

P5.6   From the results of Problem 5.5 it appears that we may apply Cramers rule to sequence convolution equations. Is this true? Verify your results.

P5.7   Use the approximation

$$S(y) \approx \frac{S(y) * [1, 1. 1, \dots]}{S_i(x)}$$

to estimate the step response of the system of Example 2.4 of Section 2.2.2. The exact values of the response $b(t)$ are given in Tables 2.4, 2.5, and 2.6. Compare your results with the exact solution and the results of Example 2.12.

P5.8   Use the data presented in Example 5.7 to determine the step response of the system (AB) with input $u(t)$ and output $u_f(t)$. Compare the results with the measured step response shown in Fig. P5.8.

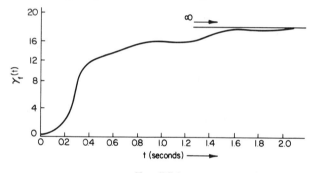

FIG. **P5.8**

P5.9   Figure P5.9 presents the input $x(t)$ and output $y(t)$ of a power system tie-line controller. Using deconvolution, estimate the controller step response.

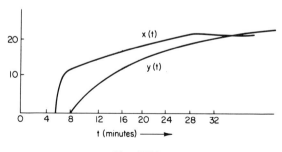

FIG. **P5.9**

P5.10 (See Unbehauen [46].) A system is to be approximated by a linear system with transfer function

$$H(s) = \frac{\displaystyle\sum_{n=0}^{7} a_n s^n}{\displaystyle\sum_{n=0}^{8} b_m s^m}$$

Determine the a_n and b_m if the step response is given by Fig. 5.10.

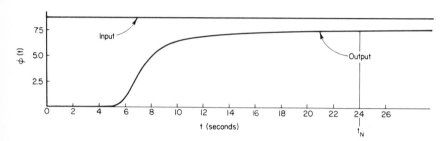

FIG. P5.10

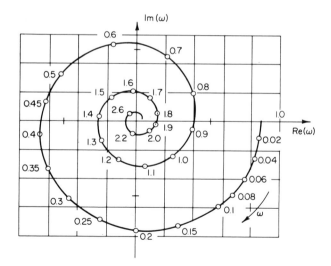

FIG. P5.10A

Evaluate the coefficients of $H(\omega)$ with $\tau = 0.5$ and

$$\int_0^\infty e^{-j\omega t} \ddot{\gamma}(t)\, dt \approx \int_0^{24} e^{-j\omega t} \ddot{\gamma}(t)\, dt$$

Answer: With 34 increments of ω between $\omega = 0$ and $\omega = 40$ and a minimum mean square fit,

$a_0 =$	0.850	$b_0 =$	1.00
$a_1 =$	-2.23	$b_1 =$	5.48
$a_2 =$	2.69	$b_2 =$	11.28
$a_3 =$	-2.03	$b_3 =$	13.90
$a_4 =$	0.992	$b_4 =$	12.70
$a_5 =$	0.0785	$b_5 =$	8.35
$a_6 =$	-0.0158	$b_6 =$	3.44
$a_7 =$	0	$b_7 =$	1.04
		$b_8 =$	0.226

P5.11 Investigate the accuracy of Tsypkin's method by application to the impulse response of a known second-order system.

P5.12 Give the formulation of Tsypkin's method if the system is to be approximated by a third-order differential equation.

P5.13 Suggest a formulation (extension) of Tsypkin's method to evaluate the coefficients of a slowly time-varying system. Discuss the difficulties in the selection of a time origin.

P5.14 Given a system with transfer function $1/(10s + 1)$ with input $x(t) = 1 - e^{-t/5}$; determine the exact output $y(t)$. For different increment sizes perform the deconvolution for the step response

$$S(y) = \frac{S(y)}{S_v(x) * [1, -1]}$$

and compare the results with the exact step response.

Partial Answer: For $\tau = 1$, deconvolution is correct to five decimal places.

P5.15 Figure P5.15 gives an excitation and response for the tie-line control of Problem 5.9. Assume that $y(s)\ (Ts + 1) = x(s)$ and apply Tsypkin's method to evaluate the system time constant. Compare the results with the result obtained in Problem 5.9.

Answer: $T = 3.5$.

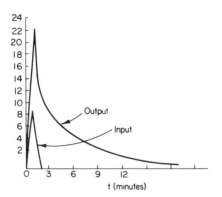

FIG. **P5.15**

P5.16   Construct $B(z)$ for the nonlinearities in Fig. P5.16 (assume $\tau g_0 = 1$).

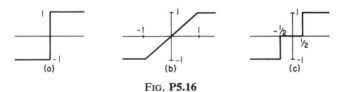

FIG. **P5.16**

P5.17   In Fig. 5.17 the system input is not the input to the nonlinear element. Set up a tabular algorithm to determine $S(x)$ for an arbitrary input sequence $S(k)$.

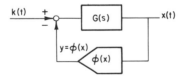

FIG. **P5.17**

P5.18   Using the tabular algorithm of Problem 5.17, determine the step response of the system in Fig. P5.17 for $G(s) = 10/s^2$, and (a) $\phi(x) = x^2 \operatorname{sgn} x$, (b) $\phi(x) = x^3$.

P5.19   Repeat Problem 5.18 for $G(s) = 1/s$.

P5.20   Consider the system shown in Fig. P5.17 where $\phi(z)$ is given by Fig. P5.16. Choose a reasonable interval size and obtain a plot of the step response for the three cases. Carry out the result sufficiently far to obtain the limit cycle, if one exists.

P5.21   It is clear from Problems 5.18 and 5.19 that the step response of the system depends greatly upon the nonlinear gain in the feedback path of the system shown in Fig. P.517. Assume that the plant $G(S)$ is fixed and linear, with impulse response $g(t)$, and the desired step response is the function $\gamma(t)$. In terms of the sequences $S(g)$ and $S(\gamma)$, construct a tabular algorithm to identify the nonlinear gain that will yield the desired step response.

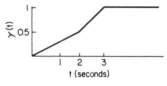

FIG. **P5.22**

P5.22   For Problem 5.21, suppose $g(t) = 5u(t)$ and $\gamma(t)$ is as shown in Fig. P5.17. Determine $\phi(x)$ from reasoning and from the results of Problem 5.20.

Index